First Fifty

A Pediatric Story

C. Charlton Mabry, M.D.

with Barbara Mabry
and Jim Niemi

Clark Publishing, Inc.
dba The Clark Group
250 East Short Street
Lexington, KY 40507
800 944 3995   info@theclarkgroupinfo.com

Visit our Web site at www.TheClarkGroupInfo.com

First Edition: July 2010

Printed in the United States of America.
10 9 8 7 6 5 4 3 2 1

ISBN: 978-0-9825057-7-9

Book & cover design by Kelly Elliott

Cover image: *The Head of a Boy by the Flemish painter, Peter Paul Rubens (1577-1640)*

Special thanks to the University of Kentucky and Lee Thomas Photography.

Lexington, Kentucky

This history is about many strands of activity woven together like a loomed, complexly patterned scarf, revealing some strands ending and others starting or restarting. It is a history written by a weaver as he saw it from the fourth floor of University Hospital and the second floor of Kentucky Clinic. It is a microcosm of all the hospital's activity because, on any given day, 10 to 20 percent of patients were babies and children.

ACKNOWLEDGMENTS

The impetus for this history came from J. Timothy Bricker, M.D., the Baylor University pediatric cardiologist who came to Kentucky as our new Chairman of the Department of Pediatrics in 2004. He has been impressed to learn that this College of Medicine, brand new in 1960 and perched on the edge of Central Appalachia, has developed, matured, and been so successful. He expressed his fears that our history would be lost or unappreciated unless recorded before everyone has passed on. So we do this now, since 2010 is the Golden Anniversary of our Department of Pediatrics. As the longest survivor – 50 years – I was handed the job.

I am indebted to others who have helped carry out this project. Foremost, I am indebted to my wife, Barbara Mabry, a former English professor and lifelong poet and writer, who has advised and edited my writing all these years—and especially this book. Next, I am hugely indebted to Jim Niemi, a former public school teacher, newspaper reporter, writer, and editor. He conducted the interviews, advised me, and has taken care of numerous details. Add to this list Linda Niemi, a newspaper and business information researcher who contributed needed public information. Florence Huffman, president of The Clark Group, Lexington, Ky., is gambling on the success of this publication.

Finally, I am indebted to the 45 past and present faculty whose tenures in our department are spread over the past 50 years for granting hour-long interviews about their parts in our history. Their oral histories, in written form, will be passed on to the Kentucky Oral History Commission, a nationally recognized program with storage at various Kentucky colleges and universities, for future use. Those who granted these oral histories are:

Robert Baumann, M.D.

Robert Beargie, M.D.

Philip Bernard, M.D.

Jeffrey Bennett, M.D.

J. Timothy Bricker, M.D., MBA

Christopher Boarman, M.D.

Robert Broughton, M.D.

Craig Carter, D.O.

Carol Cottrill, M.D.

Douglas Cunningham, M.D.

J. Steve Davis, M.D.

John Githens, M.D.

Donna Grigsby, M.D.

William Hathaway, M.D.

Bryan Hall, M.D.

Irene Hong-McAtee, M.D.

Jamshed Kanga, M.D.

Shibani Kanungo, M.D.

Stefan Kiessling, M.D.

Robert Kuhn, RPh

Vipul Mankad, M.D.

John Mink, DDS

Jeffrey Moscow, M.D.

Christopher Nelson, M.D.

Jacqueline Noonan, M.D.

Hatim Omar, M.D.

Andrew Pulito, M.D.

William Riley, M.D.

Harohalli Shashidhar, M.D.

W. Jackson Smith, M.D.

Carol Steltenkamp, M.D.

Carmel Wallace, M.D.

Peter Wong, M.D.

It has been a yearlong effort for us to bring this written history to completion, but a joy to witness how our department has developed on its way to being a Top Twenty department in a Top Twenty university—someday.

C. Charlton Mabry
Active Emeritus Professor of Pediatrics
August 2010

This book is dedicated to the children of Kentucky.

CONTENTS

><>< ><

"The countless small actions of unknown people lie at the roots
of any great moments of history."

— Howard Zinn, author
A People's History of the United States

Hollow to Hospital

Our country's success in World War II changed our vision—we saw needs and problems as things that could be fixed. Here in Kentucky, one of those needs was to bring health care to rural Kentuckians. Gov. Albert B. "Happy" Chandler was passionate about this: during his campaign for governor in 1955, he stumped from the courthouse steps in all 120 Kentucky counties, promising to bring them "doctors." True to his promise and his dream, he fired up the 1956 General Assembly, then meeting only every two years, to appropriate an initial $5 million for the establishment of a medical school at the University of Kentucky in Lexington. The University of Louisville and its medical school were not part of the state educational system at the time. Happy had always been at political odds with Louisville politicians—and other Louisville agendas in general. The medical center, later to bear Happy's name, was the second university-based medical center to be established in the United States after World War II. It is interesting that prior to WWII, there were only 60 medical schools in the country; now there are 129.

Following the appropriation, the first step was to find a medical educator to provide direction and leadership to the project. William R. Willard, M.D., who was stalled in a similar endeavor at the private University of Syracuse, was selected in the fall of 1956. He quickly assembled a diverse team, which included Howard Bost, Ph.D., medical economist; Ed Pellegrino, M.D., recently a rural medical care-delivery expert; Robert Straus, Ph.D., sociologist; Richard Noback, M.D., a medical administrator; and Allen Ross, Ph.D., a statistician with expertise in financing. They studied the existing conditions and medical needs of Kentucky, planned the facility, and began recruiting the initial basic science faculty. The UK College of Medicine admitted its first class of medical students, a total of 36, four years later, in 1960. At that milepost, as the recruitment of clinicians began, so the Department of Pediatrics' story begins.

In the fall of 1960, Dr. Straus met with John Githens, M.D., a pediatric hematologist, at the University of Colorado in Denver, actually interviewing him at the airport. After

"The Boomerangs," this piece is Duality, by Amarigo J. Brioschi, who explains that the rising form symbolizes "the epitome of heights man has reached," while the downward-pointing form represents "man's mediocrity, his failures, and disappointments." It is currently being restored and refurbished to stand with the new hospital in 2011.

University of Kentucky Medical Center at time of dedication September 23, 1960. Though completed on the outside, it was not finished on the inside until two years later.

negotiations, Githens accepted the chairmanship of the Department of Pediatrics and moved to Lexington in December of 1960. At the time, the medical school building and University Hospital had not been completed. Githens began his work by hiring a secretary but found himself very much alone on the fourth floor of the medical school. Though the offices had been completed, the laboratories had been only shelled in. From his vantage point on the fourth floor, he could look out the window at the new sculpture—the "boomerangs" that have continued to be our symbol and logo for the College of Medicine, though they have been moved twice. Githens began his initial recruitment of faculty in December 1960.

At that time (1961), the official infant death rate (birth to age one year) in Kentucky was 17 per 1,000, whereas the rate is now 7.5 per 1,000. Actually, the 1961 count was low because, in many rural areas, premature infants who did not survive were not reported. There were only a few board-certified pediatricians in Central and Eastern Kentucky when Githens began traveling and meeting with community leaders and pediatricians in Central and Eastern Kentucky. Convinced of the need, he was to assemble the first faculty for the Department of Pediatrics within the next nine months.

CHAPTER 1

Baby Milk

When I was inducted into the American Pediatric Society in 1968, I was given the history of American pediatrics, which claimed that our specialty grew out of the milk clinics of New York City in the early 20th century. After some research, I found that a similar process was occurring here in Lexington at the same time, most likely with neither knowing about the other.

Our pediatric-practice roots in Lexington go back to the Baby Milk Supply Association, founded in 1914 by several prominent local ladies, led by Mrs. Emma Haggin. Initially, they provided milk, cod liver oil, and some food to babies and young children from indigent families. Early on, they set up operations at 108 Mechanic Street, near Transylvania University.

In the first years of the Baby Milk Association/Baby Health Clinic, the milk available for distribution was either raw milk or buttermilk, mostly the latter. As local dairies churned milk to make butter, the left-over liquid was distributed as inexpensive buttermilk. In Lexington, up into the 1940s, some people bought raw milk or even milked their own cows. At one time, even people living in the best part of town kept and milked cows. Fresh milk was the best milk, it was thought.

The History of Baby Health Service

Baby Health Service (BHS) originated as Baby Milk Supply in 1914 under the guidance of five of Lexington's finest ladies with the goal of supplying formula for some of Lexington's neediest families. Lore has it that these ladies would deliver the milk and find a sick child and arrange for a doctor-friend to see the child. The clinic evolved in the 1930s at Good Samaritan Hospital. The move was made to the St. Joseph Hospital (SJH) campus in the early 1960s after SJH moved from West

Second Street to Harrodsburg Road. We have been on the SJH campus since then.

We provide free care to the children of Central Kentucky whose families make too much money to qualify for Medicaid but can't quite afford private insurance. The children receive their well-child checkups, immunizations, sick visits, labs and x-rays, and medicines. They receive top-quality care of which we are justifiably proud. Staffed by two nurses, a nurse practitioner and volunteer physicians, we are open every Monday-Friday from 7:30 a.m.-noon. We also have a backup cadre of specialty physicians who see to more complicated issues such as dermatology, urology, ENT, etc.

The BHS Board, which consists of 50 women who serve three-year terms, work daily in the clinic to assist the nurses with chart retrieval, filing, and other tasks. In addition, the BHS Board does two fund drives—individual and corporate—each year to help defray the sizeable costs. In addition, the Lexington-Fayette County Government gives financial support, we apply for grants, and we can never forget the great contribution that SJH makes to our cause in the form of free rent, maintenance of our facility, and lab and x-ray discounts. Somehow, we always seem to make our goal and don't turn away children in our socio-economic parameters.

In 1997, BHS received a Presidential Service Award from Pres. Bill Clinton at a ceremony in Philadelphia—a great tribute. While we don't do our work for awards, it is nice when we receive one of this magnitude.

We have no advertising budget; mostly we are known by word-of-mouth and publications such as the *Chevy Chaser* magazine, which lets our story be told.

We are at 1590 Harrodsburg Road in the back/basement. Phone (859) 278-1781. Come by and learn more about us.

Bill Underwood, M.D.

❖ ❖

Pasteurization was first used in the United States in the 1890s (after the development of the germ theory) to control the hazards of highly contagious bacterial diseases, including bovine tuberculosis, brucellosis, typhoid, and other salmonella strains—some of the diseases thought to be easily transmitted to humans through the drinking of raw milk. Beginning in the largest cities, pasteurization of milk slowly spread, so that almost all milk now sold in the entire United States is pasteurized.

The move for safer milk began in Lexington in August 1930 during a severe drought. Below is an excerpt from the Aug. 14, 1930, *Lexington Leader*:

City Milk Must Be Pasteurized
An official order directing that all milk be pasteurized before it is offered for sale on the Lexington market was unanimously adopted at a meeting of the city board of health late Wednesday afternoon at city hall. The order was to become effective within the next 48 hours. This action was deemed necessary to safeguard the health of residents of the city, due to the low stage of stock water and unsanitary conditions found at some dairy plants, resulting from the prolonged drouth.

Apparently, however, Lexington dairies and citizens did not really immediately comply to this new ordinance, so City Council took it up again.

Excerpt from the Oct. 8, 1930, *Lexington Leader*:

New Milk Code Is Adopted by Commissioners
Modeled after the standard milk code, recommended by the United States public health service and the state board of health, now in force in a number of states and many of the leading cities, a new milk ordinance, which it is expected will insure Lexington consumers a supply of pure and wholesome milk in the future, was submitted and passed by the board of city commissioners at a special session today.

Still, after the second city ordinance on milk pasteurization in 1930, an updated ordinance passed on Feb. 26, 1935. They persisted:

New Milk Code Passed by City
A new milk code for Lexington was passed at Monday night's meeting of the board of commissioners. The measure, introduced and given its first reading last week, lays down regulations for the proper labeling of milk and milk products, methods of pasteurization, inspection of dairies and milk plants and construction of future dairies and plants.

Since breast-feeding was not in vogue in the 1930s, the pasteurization saga was especially relevant to pediatricians of that era.

Pasteurization, as most already know, is mild heat treatment of a liquid food or beverage for a specified period of time in order to enhance its keeping qualities and to destroy pathogenic microorganisms. With respect to milk, the U.S. Public Health Service specifically defines pasteurization as the process of heating every particle of milk to at least 143 degrees F (61.7 degrees C) and holding at such temperature continuously for at least 30 minutes (low-temperature, holding method) or to at least 161 degrees F (71.7 degrees C) and holding for at least 15 seconds (high temperature, short time-period). Such treatment destroys potential spoilage-causing microorganisms, including mycobacterium tuberculosis. Most of the potential spoilage microorganisms are destroyed, thus resulting in a prolonged keeping time of the milk.

The raw-versus-pasteurized debate continues, with various non-official organizations or people touting the health benefits of raw milk as greater than the disease threat. They claim, moreover, that the purity of milk is only as good as the cleanliness of the cows and dairy from which the milk comes.

The infant feeding practices that I have observed since coming on the pediatric scene have cycled from formula feeding to a new (again) emphasis on breast feeding. In the 1950s, it was standard to make a baby's formula at home as follows:

1. Boil the bottles and rubber nipples
2. One 13-ounce can of condensed milk
3. Add 13 ounces of boiled water
4. Add 2 tablespoons of Karo syrup
5. Mix and feed

My wife reminds me that after our babies were switched from breast to bottles, I insisted that bottles and contents be sterilized until they were weaned to a cup.

From the late 1950s until the present, almost all infant formulas have been commercially made, marketed aggressively, and advertised heavily on radio and television. In the 1960s, the competition to discharge our newborns on a specified formula was branded "kick-back" by some because of the benefits the company's area salesmen would offer.

More recently, the push has been to get more mothers to breast feed because breast milk is the natural food for full-term infants during the first months of life. It is always available at the proper temperature and requires no preparation time. It is fresh and free of contaminating bacteria; therefore, there is less chance of gastrointestinal infections or disturbances for most breast-fed babies.

The breast feeding movement is institutionalized by the La Leche League, an active promoter of breast feeding. The organization maintains that breast feeding difficulties are outweighed by problems caused by cow's milk protein allergy and other intolerances to

English twins 7 months (1930). Baby Milk Supply was fascinated with twins. Its records have many photographs of twins that used their milk and clinics. *Photo courtesy Baby Milk Supply.*

Julian Estill, "station physician," examining young child at first clinic held by Baby Milk Supply, 1922. Vaccinations were administered. Note infant scales. *Photo courtesy Baby Milk Supply.*

Baby Milk Supply Waiting Room, 1922. *Photo courtesy Baby Milk Supply.*

Vincent twins 14 months (1930).

BHS nurses made home visits to children "at risk" for health and nutrition problems.

Mother and child in their shanty on Winchester Pike visited by Baby Health Service Nurse.

Mary H. born March 26, 1935, weight 6 lbs. 12 oz. August 6, weight 6 lbs. 5 oz. Treatment started August 26.

Mary H. November 6, weight 13 lbs. 1 oz. Treatment success for a difficult-to-feed baby.

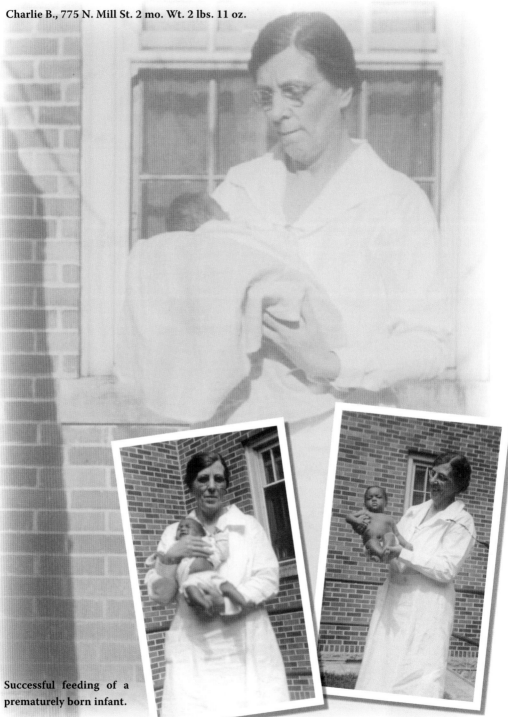

Charlie B., 775 N. Mill St. 2 mo. Wt. 2 lbs. 11 oz.

Successful feeding of a prematurely born infant.

Charlie B., 6 mo. Wt. 10 lbs. 4 oz.

Charlie B., 9 mo. Wt. 13 lbs. 11 oz.

bovine milk—less likely in breast-fed babies. But research on milk also suggests that raw human or cow's milk has an immune-boosting substance that prevents people from getting sick. Some of the studies suggest that some of these protective factors are milk sugars that bind receptor sites in our intestine where germs like to bind and start infections. Other protective factors include bacterial and viral antibodies.

So the debate continues.

>‹ ›‹

In the 1920s, as Lexington grew and the needs of the community changed, Baby Milk Supply added registered nurses to administer free immunizations and a weekly medical clinic for indigent babies and children through age twelve years. The medical clinics were staffed by general practice M.D.s, who also cared for babies and children in their private practices. In the 1930s and 1940s, the activities of Baby Milk Supply increased, as did the provision of milk, food, and medical services, and, in 1956, the name was changed to Baby Health Service, by which it is known today.

In 1935, the first two trained pediatricians arrived in Lexington: Richard Elliott, M.D., and Robert Warfield, M.D. Both had been born and raised in Lexington, and both had been trained "up East," Elliott in New Orleans, Cincinnati, and New York and Warfield in Philadelphia. They set up their separate practices in houses on Second Street between Broadway and Limestone Street, both near Baby Milk Supply on Mechanic Street.

Dr. J. Timothy Bricker, current chairman of the Department of Pediatrics at UK, spoke in October 2009 about Elliott's contributions to medical care for children:

In some ways for both the private pediatricians and the university pediatricians, Dr. Richard Elliott is our father because he is not only the first in private practice, but also one of the first advocates for a university hospital and university care of children in Lexington.

Preschooler on the stoop, 1931. Waiting for buttermilk (near Transylvania College).

The fact that over this next year we will be having an endowed Richard Elliott Professorship will be a celebration for the private community, as well as for the university community. That it will forever be a professorship held by the chief of General Academic Pediatrics who will be a general pediatrician is a celebration where things have come full circle with hopefully what in the 1950s Dr. Elliott's dream for us was. As I have learned more about the history of pediatrics in Lexington, in some ways Dr. Elliott was really our first chairman, even though we did not have a medical school yet.

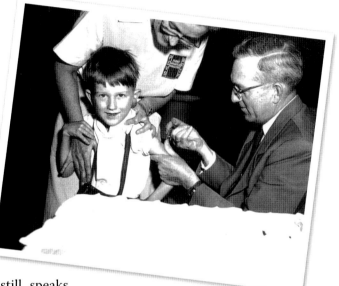

Richard G. Elliott, M.D., first board-certified pediatrician in Lexington (1935), administering Salk polio vaccine in April 1954 vaccine drive at BHS. Mrs. James Malloy, director of BHS, supporting.

It is significant that most pediatricians left the AMA Section on Pediatrics in 1931 to form their own organization, the American Academy of Pediatrics, which still speaks for pediatrics today. The issue was that the AMA would not sanction free immunizations administered in local public health departments or free clinics such as Baby Milk Supply. Elliott and Warfield retained both their American Medical Association and American Academy of Pediatrics memberships and dual loyalties.

About this time, when Emma Haggin's daughter, Betty Haggin Mallory, took over much of the leadership of Baby Milk Supply, a cluster of pediatric practices began to develop up and down Second Street. Pediatricians who opened there in 1935 were:

- Richard Elliott, M.D., Vanderbilt University, Nashville
- Robert Warfield, M.D., University of Pennsylvania, Philadelphia
- Alex Alexander, M.D., Johns Hopkins, Baltimore

Later in that decade, still other trained pediatricians also came to Second Street:

- Carolyn Scott, M.D., University of Cincinnati, Cincinnati

- William Maxon, M.D., University of Michigan, Ann Arbor
- Carl Wheeler, M.D., University of Louisville, Louisville

They had their separate offices, typically in older houses on Second Street between Broadway and Limestone Street, clustered around Gratz Park—a pediatric ghetto!

They did not seem to be in competition. Collegiality was exciting. When other pediatricians arrived in Lexington before the University of Kentucky Department of Pediatrics began in 1960, however, they located their offices near the two new hospitals, St. Joseph on Harrodsburg Road and Central Baptist on Nicholasville Road in south Lexington:

- Joan Rider, M.D., Down-State, New York
- Howard Rippy, M.D., Vanderbilt, Nashville
- Carl Scott, M.D., University of Louisville, Louisville
- Noble Macfarlane, M.D., University of Virginia, Charlottesville
- Dennis Penn, M.D., University of Louisville, Louisville
- Jeffrey Blackerby, M.D., University of Louisville, Louisville

Giving out toys at Christ Episcopal Church at Christmas Baby Health Service for indigents, 1937-1939. BHS Director, Mrs. James Malloy; in flowered dress.

Baby Milk Supply monthly budget, 1936.

All of these doctors were in private solo practice, except for Dr. Macfarlane, who joined the Lexington Clinic as its first pediatrician. Their typical staff were a nurse and a receptionist. Their equipment usually included hand instruments that they carried in their black doctor's bag, scales, autoclave, an eye chart on the wall, two examining rooms, and a gurney. If an x-ray or laboratory work was needed, they were sent to one of the three hospitals—St. Joseph, Good Samaritan, or Central Baptist. All the pediatricians admitted patients and were on staff at all three hospitals. Moveover, all, except for the allergists, made house calls and were on call all of the time, 24/7. Surely, they must have sometimes covered for one another.

From this group of pediatricians, Richard Elliott emerged as dean. A native Lexingtonian with a stellar academic record, Elliott graduated from Vanderbilt Medical School in 1932. From there, he was a rotating intern at Charity Hospital in New Orleans, then had a year of pediatric residency at Cincinnati Children's Hospital and a final year in New York—sterling credentials, along with his pediatric board certification.

Children's ward at Good Samaritan Hospital (circa 1950) where most children were hospitalized in Lexington prior to 1962.

Actually, pediatrics as a specialty was beginning to catch on outside of Lexington and Louisville. Bryan Hall, M.D., recently retired from our Department of Pediatrics, writes that there was a similar start-up in his hometown, Paintsville:

> *My father, Dr. Lon C. Hall, was the first pediatrician to practice in Eastern Kentucky. His practice started in 1939 in Paintsville, Ky. At that time there were no antibiotics or scalp vein intravenous needles for children. Consequently, many of his patients with serious infections and dehydration died as he helplessly observed.*
>
> *Even after antibiotics became available, as well as infant scalp vein needles, there were still children that needed to be transferred quickly, which was difficult because of poor roads, unreliable transportation and far-away children's centers in Louisville and Cincinnati. Frustrated, he designed and had built a pediatric floor on the top level of the Paintsville*

Hospital in 1953, which he staffed and to which other doctors could admit their patients for care. It had 11 beds, a treatment room and a formula room. Each patient's room had a child's bed and a bed for the mother.

He was ecstatic when the Albert B. Chandler University of Kentucky Hospital and Medical School were built. It meant he had a close referral center and an outstanding faculty to call for consultation.

Being an exceptional practitioner led Elliott to the presidency of the Fayette County Medical Society (1952) and the Kentucky State Medical Association. He was the designated liaison between the Fayette County Medical Society and the University of

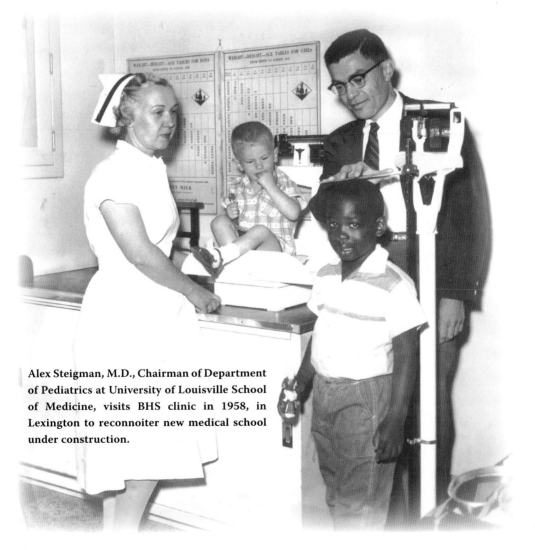

Alex Steigman, M.D., Chairman of Department of Pediatrics at University of Louisville School of Medicine, visits BHS clinic in 1958, in Lexington to reconnoiter new medical school under construction.

Kentucky's group of five planners for the Medical Center, led by Dr. William Willard. Unfortunately, Dr. Elliott died of cancer in February 1962, less than two months before the first patients were admitted to University Hospital. Most fittingly, though, his family has recently endowed the General Pediatrics Professorship Chair in the UK Department of Pediatrics. Other Elliotts have continued the medical tradition with a son, Edward (UK-MD 1979), who became a radiation oncologist, and a grandson, Daniel (UK-MD 2007), a Medical Officer for the U.S. Navy.

The momentum to have a medical school as part of the University of Kentucky in Lexington hung in the balance initially, as many doctors were fearful of the competition for private patients and wanted the appropriated money to go to their alma mater, the University of Louisville. Elliott, as president of the Fayette County Medical Society, was instrumental in getting a resolution of approval from the local medical society. Drs. Francis Massie and Edward Ray, Sr. also were leaders in the effort to get a medical school established here, as was Brick Chambers, the UK school infirmary physician.

C H A P T E R   2

Academic Startup

First of all, did Kentucky either need or want a second medical school—a university hospital? A pediatrics department?

A needs assessment for doctors for Kentucky in 1955, just prior to the initial funding of the UK College of Medicine, tallied 75 pediatricians in all of Kentucky; most practiced in Louisville, and only a few served the rest of the state.

With need established, Robert Straus, a Ph.D. sociologist, was assigned to lead the recruiting of a chairman for the soon-to-be-formed Department of Pediatrics. His interest focused on Dr. Jack Githens because Githens, a laboratory researcher on bone-marrow transplantation, had started a continuity-of-care clinic for rheumatic fever and other chronic disease disorders at the University of Colorado. Dr. Straus first interviewed Dr. Githens at the Denver airport; then he and his wife visited Lexington, after which the deal was completed in October 1960.

As the new medical school began, there were no pediatric subspecialists in Lexington, except for two pediatric allergists. The decision to bring both general and advanced pediatric care to the region was timely—and welcomed by most. The local pediatric community was welcoming, though guarded, as the locals were concerned that the new Department of Pediatrics might draw their private paying patients. At the time, the older pediatricians were admitting their patients to Good Samaritan Hospital's children's ward, and the other pediatricians were using rooms on

John H. Githens, M.D.
Temple 1954 Chairman,
December 1960-June 1963

the sixth floor of the more recently built St. Joseph Hospital on Harrodsburg Road and in Central Baptist Hospital on Nicholasville Road.

Dr. Githens and family were in town and settled in as 1961 began. As he set out to recruit the initial faculty for the Department of Pediatrics, he turned first to his familiar University of Colorado pediatric faculty in Denver. Then, during the winter Western Society of Pediatric meeting and later in May at the annual National Academic Pediatric meetings in Atlantic City—the Society for Pediatric Research and the American Pediatric Society—he talked with and interviewed various candidates. In the ensuing months, those who accepted moved to Lexington in this order:

December 1960—John H. Githens, M.D.—Chairman, Professor of Pediatrics, Temple University (1945), from University of Colorado (hematology).

March 1961—Fredrick A. Horner, M.D.—Associate Professor of Pediatrics—University of Rochester (1947), Associate Professor of Pediatrics from University of Colorado (neurology).

April 1961—Thomas L. Nelson, M.D.—Associate Professor of Pediatrics—University of California at San Francisco (1946), Superintendent of Sonoma St. Hospital and School (allergy).

April 1961—Wylda Hammond, M.D. (Nelson's wife)—Assistant Professor of Pediatrics, University of California at San Francisco (1949), from the medical staff at Sonoma St. Hospital and School (handicapped children) assigned to and funded by the Division of Maternal and Child Health, Department of Health, Frankfort, Ky. In 1961 there were rigid nepotism rules at the university, thus Dr. Hammond had to be based in another organization.

May 1961—William E. Hathaway, M.D.—University of Oklahoma (1954), Instructor in Pediatrics, former Fellow in Hematology under Githens, then private practice of pediatrics in Colorado Springs, Colo. (hematology).

July 1961—C. Charlton Mabry, M.D.—Emory University (1954), Instructor in Pediatrics, from NIH Fellowship at St. Christopher's Hospital for Children, Temple University, Philadelphia, Pa. (endocrinology and metabolism).

July 1961—Robert W. Chamberlain, M.D.—Harvard University (1956), Instructor in Pediatrics from training program in behavioral pediatrics at Boston Children's Hospital, Instructor in Pediatrics (behavioral pediatrics).

August 1961—Kenneth W. Dumars, M.D.—University of Colorado (1945), from private practice of pediatrics, Colorado Springs, Colo. Assistant Professor of

First Faculty, June 1962

First row, left to right: Shirley Hurst, staff secretary; Jackie Noonan, M.D., Cardiology; Jack Githens, M.D., Chairman; department secretary; Donna Hall, staff secretary.

Middle row: Robert Chamberlain, M.D., Behavioral Pediatrics; James Wilhite, M.D., PT General Pediatrics; Tom Nelson, M.D., Allergy.

Back row: William Hathaway, M.D., Hematology; staff secretary; staff secretary; Charlton Mabry, M.D., Genetics/Endocrinology/Metabolism; Jack Boehm, M.D., Nursery, soon to leave to be first neonatologist at Northwestern University.

Pediatrics and Chief of Staff at Cardinal Hill Convalescent Hospital (handicapped children). Dr. Dumars had established a reputation of being about the only pediatrician in that part of Colorado who could care for chronically ill children (chronic care, cytogenetics).

December 1961—Jacqueline A. Noonan, M.D.—University of Vermont (1954), Assistant Professor of Pediatrics from University of Iowa (cardiology).

When this first pediatric faculty of eight was assembled in 1961, we were a restless bunch of young clinicians, most having just come from very active training programs.

But there were no patients as yet. And since some of the town pediatricians were suspicious of our presence, it was politic not to mess with any of the Lexington pediatric patients. We were only rarely asked to see any of their patients in consultation, and they still referred problem patients to Louisville and to Cincinnati.

On a Monday morning in fall 1961, Jack Githens couldn't wait to tell me about his weekend adventure. He had attended, by invitation from Mary Breckinridge, the 36th annual meeting of the Frontier Nursing Service in Wendover, Ky. Breckinridge was from a prominent Arkansas political family and had been educated at finishing schools in Switzerland and Connecticut.

After her first husband died in 1906, Breckinridge remarried in 1914 and had two children who died at very young ages. The second marriage did not last, and she took back her maiden name. She went into volunteer service to assist in France's recovery from World War I, then to England for training to become a certified nurse-midwife. With her strong sense of social obligation, she somehow found her way to mountainous southeast Kentucky, where she established the Frontier Nursing Service (FNS) near Hyden in Leslie County in 1925.

From her headquarters at Wendover, several miles south of Hyden, she and the nursing service provided midwifery and general nursing care over a large area—Leslie County and adjacent parts of nearby counties—usually on horseback. All during Githens' visit, Breckinridge and her board members (Louisville and Lexington bankers and donors) railed against "those damn people"—U.S. Corps of Engineers employees who had just surveyed the boundaries of the soon-to-be-constructed Buckhorn dam and lake. The lake was to back up almost to her doorstep at Wendover and would make numerous dirt roads and trails inaccessible. "Those damn people" brought a giggle from the board members, which provoked her to reuse the phrase again and again. Soon after Githens' visit, Breckinridge changed from horses to Jeeps, but kept a barn for the retired horses.

The dam was built for flood control but became the centerpiece for a Kentucky State Park. Breckinridge died in 1965 at the age of 84, but there are remnants of FNS still in operation, mostly nursing outposts. Babies are now delivered at the relatively new Mary Breckinridge Hospital, built soon after her death in Hyden, a stone's throw from Wendover. Breckinridge would undoubtedly be pleased that "her" hospital is one of 66 birthing hospitals remaining in Kentucky today.

In 1963, when Dr. Jack Greene, the newly appointed chairman of the UK Department of Obstetrics and Gynecology, was invited to join the FNS Board of Directors, he declined, not wanting to promote the practice of midwifery. Rather, he felt it his job to train obstetricians for delivering babies. Professional deliveries were infrequent in mountain and rural areas.

Just last year, a refrigerator repairman came to my home to fix my icemaker. He told me about his growing up in a hollow, the Yeaddiss community on the north side of Big Laurel Mountain in Leslie County. Now in his 40s, he attended Leslie County schools through grade school, then as a young adult he went to a Letcher County vocational school. He was able to hitch a daily ride on the grade-school bus to the county line, then walk on in to Whitesburg to vocational school, reversing the process in the afternoon. After finishing appliance repair training, he moved to Irvine, where he now lives and commutes 50 miles to Lexington for his job.

He told me that he never saw nor was examined by a doctor until he moved to Irvine. Rather, all of his health care was delivered by Barbara French, an LPN with FNS, at Cutshin Clinic farther down their hollow. He remembered receiving immunizations, penicillin shots, school physicals, and other medical help at Cutshin Clinic. The same LPN is still at the Cutshin FNS station. In great anguish, he remembered a teenage friend, victim of an accidental shooting, being taken to the Cutshin FNS station and bleeding to death before he could be moved to a hospital. The roads now are much improved, and you would not stop at Cutshin outreach clinic if such an accident were to reoccur.

Finding trained professionals to deliver babies from poor families has always been a problem everywhere. Before the opening of University of Kentucky Hospital in 1962, the city of Lexington assumed that UK Hospital would take on this responsibility for its poor. Our hospital administrators balked. So eventually, the city hired a doctor to do home deliveries for indigent mothers. Dr. Greene commented that it looked to him

James W. Hammons, D.O.,
Outpatient obstetrics
Courtesy Lexington Herald-Leader

In response to University Hospital administration's refusal to deliver babies of indigent mothers, the Lexington City Council adopted an ordinance that the Health Department hire a doctor to make the necessary home deliveries. It hired James W. Hammons, D.O., a black osteopath, who had opened his office on West Third Street in 1959. Already he had been making some home deliveries in his neighborhood. Dr. Hammons once stated "back then doctors got $35 for delivering a white child and $25 for delivering a Negro baby, and in that era there were some things you just had to accept, whether you liked it or not." Hammons became respected, not only in the black community but in the eyes of the Fayette County Medical Society (FCMS). Through the efforts of the president of FCMS, Dr. David Hull, Hammons became the first black member of the FCMS and the Kentucky Medical Society in 1968. Subsequently, he was allowed to see patients and check their charts at Central Baptist Hospital, but not allowed to write on the charts. He continued to care for patients until he died at age 79.

as if he would have to deliver babies in the fountain in front of the hospital, because they were coming, and the hospital wasn't going to allow their admission. Actually, my first patient with galactosemia was delivered in the back seat of a taxi outside the door to our emergency room. As the years rolled on, we developed a completely open-door policy—all comers are welcomed without question.

Dr. Githens developed a good relationship with Dr. Helen Frazer, the director of Maternal and Child State Health Department at the capital. Githens, knowing that our hospital and clinics would not open until the spring of 1962, and having a concern for undoctored children, proposed that Dr. Frazer support a general pediatric traveling clinic funded by the State Health Department. When Dr. Frazer scraped up some money, we began with the first monthly clinic, held in Prestonsburg, Floyd County. I once described the very first traveling clinic:

> On a chilly Wednesday in September 1961, I was one of three pediatricians, with a small support staff, who rolled out of Lexington before dawn and arrived four hours later at the Floyd County Health Department. We were greeted by children and parents in a full waiting room (some waiting outside) as well as health nurses, the Mayor (John R. Archer, M.D.) and the County Judge Executive (Slick Stumbo). Each of us from the new medical school in Lexington was carefully scrutinized; this was a new outreach program for all concerned.
>
> The children were examined and evaluated one at a time and lunch for all was brought. Medical problems ranged from simple impetigo to neurologic deficits and severe cardiac sequelae of rheumatic fever. By the end of the day, we had earned the respect of the families and officials, and we had come to appreciate the high value and respect the adults placed on their children. We also felt that we had made a very good beginning.

This first clinic set the tone and has allowed us, over the years, to continue and to expand pediatric traveling clinics. These clinics were important because at that time fewer than 3,000 doctors practiced in Kentucky—today there are more than 8,000—with Eastern Kentucky's having the fewest doctors per patient in the state. Even today, however, many of the children in the area clinics still have not received care from a pediatric specialist, much less a subspecialist. Over the years, the clinics have also offered subspecialty care, including cardiology, neurology, genetics, diabetes and pulmonology—bringing advanced medical care to young patients across Kentucky. To date, pediatricians from Kentucky Children's Hospital have seen children in more than 2,300 individual clinics all across Eastern and Southeastern Kentucky.

During 1961, when there were no intramural patients, we were still very busy. Drs. Githens and Hathaway and I were working in our research laboratories, and all of us were made members of various hospital and medical school committees. My assignment was to the Medical Records Committee, the Pharmacy Committee, and the Clinical Laboratory Committee. One of my memories of the Medical Records Committee is that we met monthly and wrangled for several hours each time about how to make the very best medical record. Much of the debate, I recall, centered on the rag content of the history and physical forms. I think that we ultimately decided that the rag content must be 45 percent. We also were charged by various administrators to make the very best procedure manuals, starting from scratch, and we were not to import manuals from other institutions—our chance, they said, to do everything right.

One of my other assignments was the Pharmacy Committee, where the goal was to create a core list of drugs for the pharmacy that would not be duplicates, in order to keep a very effective and cost-containing pharmacy. The concept sounded very good, but I remember when one of our cardiac surgeons became exasperated, stood up, and announced that he was not going to let anyone else tell him what drugs he could prescribe and stomped out of the meeting, never to return. There have, of course, been many advances in drugs—availability, use, and delivery—over 50 years.

My next assignment was to the Clinical Laboratory Committee as chairman. Since we were not yet caring for any patients in our hospital or clinics, I never bothered to call a meeting. This decision later blew up as we first started seeing patients in 1962 when there was a dramatic confrontation between the Chairman of Medicine and the Chairman of Pathology over whether or not he (medicine) could get a protein-bound iodine measurement (the closest thing to measuring thyroid hormone at the time) on the weekend. I remember this well because Dean Willard called me to his office and ordered me to hold the first Clinical Laboratory Committee meeting. This meeting never happened—the two made up.

While serving as an National Institute of Health (NIH) postdoctoral fellow in Philadelphia, I had set up paper chromatography for amino acid analysis on blood and urine. To process a specimen required three days. The first column chromatography equipment was just being developed by the Phoenix Company in Philadelphia. The prototype equipment filled up most of the room. As I was leaving St. Christopher's, I decided to try high-voltage paper electrophoresis to speed the process to about 6-8 hours. So, using my laboratory start-up allowance and in a new setting, I purchased pieces of equipment from a scientific supply house and the rest from Sears and Roebuck. It worked.

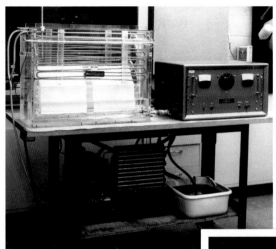

High Voltage Paper Electrophoresis (HVPE), apparatus built by C. Mabry with parts from Sears, Roebuck and Co. and a small laboratory supply company (Savant). The device was used to screen babies and children with various disabilities in serum or urine. This apparatus reduced running time using paper chromatography from 2 1/2 days to 2 1/2 hours. Specimens are now sent to out-of-state reference and commercial laboratories. The 1960's was an era of building your own laboratory equipment (supported by NIH grant).

Technician applying samples to HVPE support paper. HVPE is a rapid method for partitioning and locating amino acids, sugars, indoles, purines, pyrimidines, acids of the citric cycle, phenolic acids, keto acids and imidazoles in biologic fluids. When standards are run, their concentrations can be estimated and measured by densitometer. HVPE was used in our Central Clinical Laboratory and available for hospital-wide use from 1964-1974. Thereafter, specimens were sent to outside reference and specialty labs.

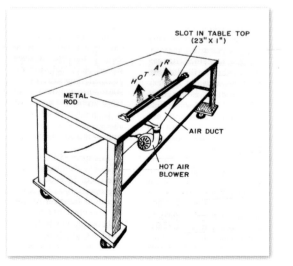

Pipetting table for rapid drying of specimen applications. Fabricated from Sears, Roebuck and Co. materials. Casters allow for closet storage when not in use.

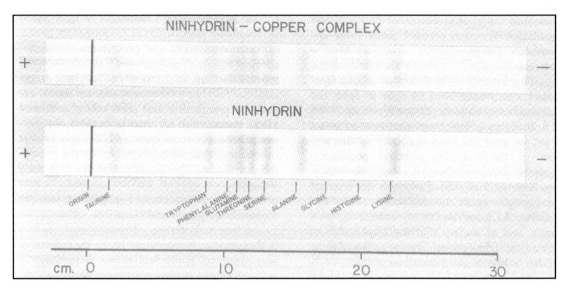

High-voltage electophoretic separation of selected amino acids at 1500 volts x 90 min. Bands show the relative intensities of the ninhydrin and ninhydrin-copper development. The former locating reagent fades over a period of days, the latter is permanent.

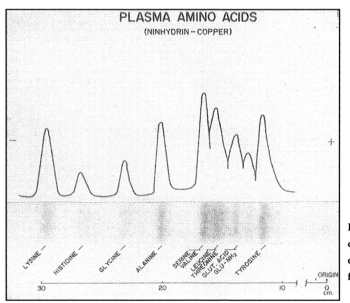

HVPE of normal plasma. Subsequent scanning with recording densitometer provides method for quantitation.

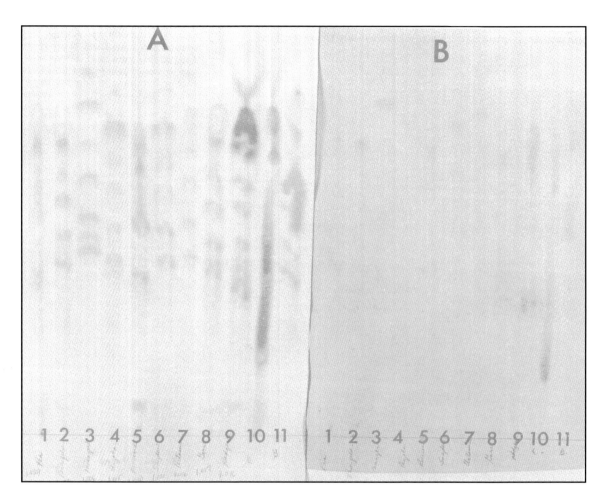

"Screening" for pathologic aminoaciduria. Duplicate HVPE separations of amino acids in 50 microliter aliquots of random urine from 11 patients (1500 volts x 90 min). Electrophoretogram (a) developed with ninhydrin; (b) developed with isatin. Eight urines on left of each electrophoretogram normal. Three urines on the right of each electrophoretogram are from patients with (9) cystinuria, (10) Fanconi syndrome, and (11) glycinemia. Specific gravity obtained on each specimen aids in estimation of amino acid concentrations. Trailing and smudging in pathologic specimens is due to overloading or large excesses of amino acid(s). Discrete patterns may be obtained with smaller volumes of urine.

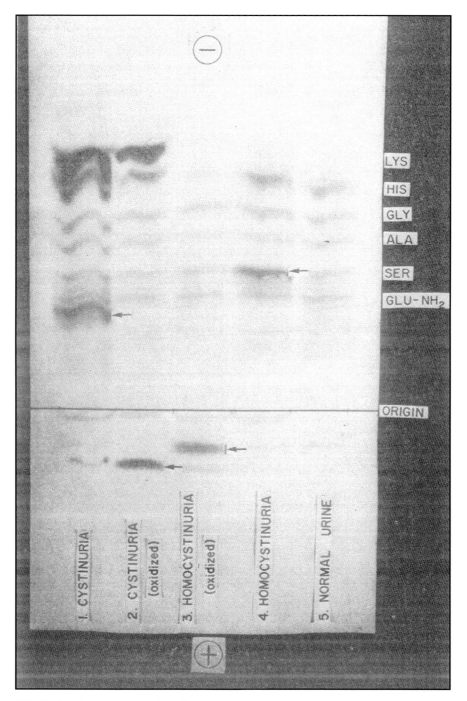

HVPE of amino acids in urines from normal, homocystinuric and cystinuri patients. Prior oxidation of urine permits better resolution and identification.

High-voltage electrophoretic separation of multiple sugars added to urine. Subsequent development and scanning with a recording desitometer provides method for quantitation.

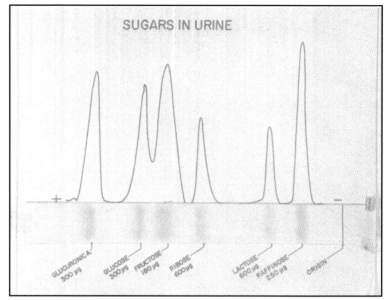

SUGARS IN URINE

GLUCURONIC A 300 µg

GLUCOSE 300 µg FRUCTOSE 180 µg

RIBOSE 600 µg

LACTOSE 600 µg RAFFINOSE 250 µg

ORIGIN

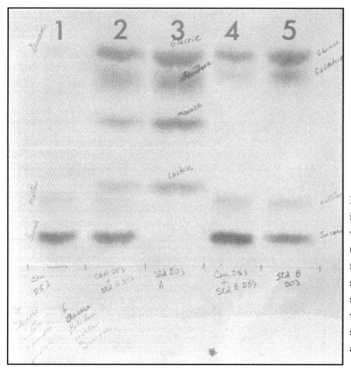

HVPE which shows how sugars in a newly marketed infant milk were identified. Left to right (1) new infant milk, (2) new infant mik with mixture of sugar standards, (3) mixture of sugar standards, (4) new infant milk with mixture or alternate sugar standards, and (5) mixture of alternate sugar standards.

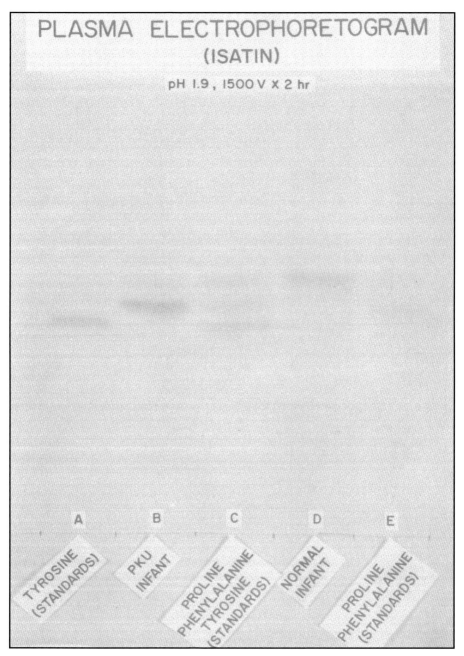

HVPE of plasma using location reagent (isatin) relatively selective for tyrosine, phenyl-alanine, and proline. Note great excess of phenylalanine and no detectable tyrosine in specimen from 10 day old PKU infant.

REFERENCES—HIGH-VOLTAGE ELECTROPHORESIS

Mabry CC, Todd WR: Quantitative measurement of individual and total free amino acids in urine; rapid method employing high-voltage paper electrophoresis and direct densitometry and its application to the urinary excretions of amino acids in normal subjects. J Lab Clin Med, 1963, 61:146-157.

Mabry CC, Gryboski JD, Karam EA: Rapid identification and measurement of mono- and oligosaccharides; an adaptation of high-voltage paper electrophoresis for sugars and its application to biologic materials. J Lab Clin Med, 1963, 72:817-830.

Mabry CC, Karam EA: Measurement of free amino acids in plasma and serum by high-voltage paper electrophoresis. Am J Clin Path, 1964, 42:421-430.

Mabry CC: High-voltage electrophoresis, in CRC Critical Reviews in Clinical Laboratory Sciences, edited by Faulkner WR, King JW, Cleveland, Chemical Rubber Co., 1970, 135-190.

All the while, there was some action going on in our three pediatric research laboratories. At the time, the pediatric academy was small, and our national meetings of the Society for Pediatric Research ("Young Turks") and the American Pediatric Society ("Old Turks") were held the first week in May. Presentations were by invitation only, and my work with high-voltage electrophoresis to replace paper chromatography was accepted for the May 1962 meeting in Atlantic City. For the next ten years, all of the clinical laboratory work at UK for amino acids and sugars was performed in my laboratory; this availability launched many of my and others' reports in the 1960s and 1970s, and put us on the map. Thereafter, Kentucky has had at least one invited presentation on the program every year.

In addition to the early work that was going on in the institution, things were happening under the administration of the first governor from Eastern Kentucky, Bert Combs. In 1961, the first segment of Kentucky's parkway system was completed, about 40 miles of road from Winchester to just beyond Campton, in Wolfe County. That road, the Bert Combs Mountain Parkway, allowed us to go to patients and for patients to come to us in much shorter periods of time. Our first clinic in Prestonsburg required four travel hours; now it takes only two hours. Dr. Noonan teamed up with an adult cardiologist, Dr. Jack Reeves, and began seeing children in separate heart clinics, the first being in Hazard. All of these clinics continue today.

The Mountain Parkway was a toll road, which was a difficulty for some families from the mountains who came to Lexington and could not afford the toll to return home. Eastern Kentucky families called it the "pay to ride" road. Faculty in the clinic would sometimes personally provide the cash for a family to travel back home.

Not all smooth waters—some were choppy. Even early on, an unexpected problem was opposition and criticism from the faculty on main campus. Naturally, they had not been included in the medical development on the south edge of their campus—actually, it was jealousy over the higher salaries of faculty ($12,000 for me) on the medical campus. Socially, it was hurtful; remnants still exist today. They did not understand that, in medicine, you have to do it to teach it and that medical training is a far longer and more costly enterprise—and that we worked all day every day—research, teaching, and, soon, seeing and caring for patients.

The year 1962 began with very cold weather and, through most of January and February, there was snow on the ground. The newly assembled pediatric faculty stayed busy by attending committee meetings that were focused on the start-up of the hospital and attending out-of-town professional meetings. I spent several weeks at Oak Ridge National Laboratories learning how to use isotopes in the research laboratory. All of us were focused on the opening of University of Kentucky Hospital on April 24, 1962. Pediatrics was assigned two rooms (unimaginable now), double occupancy, on the west wing of the fifth floor. As the date approached, the administrators wanted a very smooth, yet noteworthy, admission day, with star patients that could be publicized. Several days prior to the opening of University Hospital, we were summoned to attend a meeting in Memorial Hall with Gov. Bert Combs. We all assembled there in the early afternoon, and, since Memorial Hall had 500 seats, we were pretty much gathered down next to the stage when Governor Combs came out. I have always thought that Governor Combs was "my Governor" because he brought significant change to Kentucky. It was interesting that Gov. Happy Chandler had always been his political rival in the Democratic Party and that Governor Combs was now trumpeting the opening of the Chandler Medical Center, the first medical school in Kentucky supported by the state; the University of Louisville School of Medicine had always been a city-supported school. This arrangement lasted only until the 70s, when it too became state-assisted.

Governor Combs talked for a while, but the thing that I remember is his telling us not to be frustrated about slowness in procuring and obtaining ordinary supplies. He described the situation in his office at the Capitol: if he needed some stationery, he had to order it on a certain form and it took about seven days to get there. All the while, he could actually look out his office window at the storage site. While walking back to the Medical Center, I thought that it reminded me of Mark Twain's comment, "If the world ever ends, I want to be in Kentucky because everything there happens 20 years later than anywhere else."

But our opening can best be told by the case histories of the first two patients, children who were admitted on April 24 and 25, 1962.

> Hospital #00-00-01 M.S., born 11/14/50, was an 11 ½-year-old girl from Pikeville. She was a heart patient who as an infant had a problem with recurrent seizures or spells, and cyanosis had been noted in the neonatal period but had not recurred. As a toddler and preschooler, she tired easily and had some exertional dyspnea. Also, for an 11-year-old child, she was undergrown. She was referred to one of our pediatric traveling clinics by Dr. Rustin, the Health Officer at the Pike County Health Department. At the Prestonsburg Traveling Heart Clinic, she was seen by Dr. Noonan, who found her to be a small child with a prominent left chest and a loud heart murmur with a systolic trill that was easily palpated. The murmur transmitted both to the neck and through to her back as well as the so-obvious apex of her heart. Dr. Noonan immediately recognized that she had a large patent ductus arteriosus and referred her to our hospital for surgical correction. The chest x-ray revealed a moderately enlarged heart with prominence to the left ventricle and engorgement of the pulmonary vasculature. Her EKG was interpreted as showing left ventricular enlargement at the upper limits of normal. She was scheduled for admission on April 24, 1962, so the family with M.S. rode the bus from Pikeville to Lexington the day before and stayed overnight at the Yocum Motel across the street from University Hospital. She was admitted at 8:15 a.m. on the 24th as the first patient admitted to the new University Hospital. Two days later, she was taken to the operating room, where she was greeted by three chest surgeons and the Chief Surgical Resident. Though all were experienced with this proposed operation, it seemed as if most of the Surgery Department wanted to be there for the first surgical case at University Hospital. The procedure went well, and she was discharged to home 11 days later. Dr. Noonan has continued to follow M.S. from time to time and, most recently, at age 57, she is in good health still living in Pikeville.

It is interesting to look at the practice of medicine in 1962 versus today. At that time, M.S. was diagnosed by physical examination, using a stethoscope, came into the hospital, and had her open-chest surgery without any further tests. Today she would have had an echocardiogram to diagnose the patent ductus. She would have then undergone cardiac catheterization when the ductus could be repaired by a device, so things have really changed in the treatment of patent *ductus arteriosis*—no open chest surgery.

R.H. was the second patient admitted.

> R.H., born 07/28/59, from Hazel Green, Ky. (Wolfe County), began losing weight at age 11 months, all the while taking his milk and table food as

Pediatric Faculty, Housestaff, Head Nurse, and Play Lady. June 1963 after Grand Rounds. Dr. Githens' (front row, fourth from left) last appearance. (Note that the Medical Center boomerangs have been moved to front of building.) Back row: Three private practitioners – Bill Maxon and Jeff Blackerby, without coats, Jodi Ridge, third from right in second row.

expected. At 13 months, his parents became aware that his stools had become loose, frequent, and malodorous. By 20 months of age, these symptoms became progressively worse, so when he was 23 months of age, they took him to their nearest physician, Dr. Herschel Murray, at West Liberty in adjacent Morgan County. He found that R.H. was anemic, had a prominent abdomen and wasted extremities. Dr. Murray referred R.H. to us with the tentative diagnosis of malnourishment. The family traveled down the brand new Bert Combs Mountain Parkway on 04/25/62, and R.H. was the first patient admitted on the morning of April 25, 1962, the second child admitted to the Pediatric Service.

On admission, R.H appeared to be a very sad and withdrawn toddler. He had a greatly distended abdomen that was tympanitic and had hyperactive bowel sounds. His liver and spleen were not enlarged. His extremities were thin and wasted and throughout the first day he had frequent large foamy stools.

The initial laboratory studies confirmed that he had a mild anemia, but we focused on the probable intestinal malabsorption situation. His laboratory studies showed a hemoglobin of 10.8 grams/dL, normal electrolytes, a sweat chloride of 12 mEq/L (0-70) an increase in total stool fat, and impaired absorption of xylose.

An important step was to take a duodenal mucosal biopsy performed by the newly available Rabin tube intestinal biopsy adapted for pediatric use. The biopsy showed atrophied mucosa consistent with celiac disease. R.H. was placed on a gluten-free diet and remained in our hospital for over three months, showing steady improvement. He slowly gained 10 pounds, and his distended abdomen diminished. A repeat biopsy showed continued atrophy of the duodenal mucosa. But he was discharged to home on a gluten-free diet, to be followed here in our clinic. Soon after discharge the family moved to Ohio, so he was lost to follow-up.

When I talked recently with an adult gastroenterologist in private practice, she told me that she has a large number of patients with mild celiac disease. The patients obtain their gluten-free foods at local supermarkets. Even though clinical symptoms and serologic markers may suggest the diagnosis of celiac disease, histologic (biopsy) confirmation remains the gold standard for diagnosis.

The measurement of R.H.'s sweat chloride required some ingenuity. Obtaining sweat analysis from a patient previously had to be obtained by wrapping the patient in plastic while they lay on a heating pad. After they had perspired enough, one would unwrap them and try to recover sweat with a pipette, at least 100 mg or 0.1 mL, which was then transferred to a preweighed 2 x 2 inch gauze in a preweighed small plastic container.

Then the eluted sweat was measured for chloride content, with high levels expected in a patient with cystic fibrosis, a condition R.H., with his symptoms, might have had. But two years earlier, Drs. Gibson and Cooke at Chicago Children's Hospital had introduced a new method to collect sweat. The drug Pilocarpine was electrophoretically induced through a small area of skin, the ensuing sweat from that small area collected in a 2 x 2-inch preweighed gauze, then the chloride content measured. This was a very significant advance in detecting and caring for patients with cystic fibrosis, the most common, serious hereditary disorder in the white population. Using the blueprint and instructions provided by Drs. Gibson and Cooke's report in the Journal of Pediatrics two years later, we fabricated our own sweat chloride device with the assistance of all our medical instrumentation shop, building a small transformer with 11/4 x 11/4-inch electrodes and then using them to perform the first sweat chloride at the University of Kentucky. This specific instrument was used for the next 30 years to perform all the sweat chlorides at University Hospital, and the skin contact electrodes are still in use.

Recently we learned through several aunts and a first cousin that R.H. died in 2008 at age 50. His father died while R.H. was young, and his mother had difficulty caring for him and his siblings. R.H. was never well and never under consistent care by a physician, nor regularly employed. His celiac symptoms continued until his death. Forty-eight years ago, when R.H. was under our care, there were no serologic tests for gluten-sensitive enteropathy nor for the recently introduced DNA mutation analysis for the disorder. Antigliadin antibodies can also be present in other conditions, such as cow's milk protein enteropathy, Crohn's disease, tropical sprue, and other gastrointestinal disorders.

Antiendomysial antibodies, in the family of IgA antibodies, have a sensitivity and specificity for celiac disease approaching 100%. Together, antigliaden and endomysial antibodies have a 75%-83% predictive value for biopsy evidence of celiac disease. Based on population studies with these antibodies, we now estimate that the prevalence of celiac disease is much higher than previous estimates based on biopsy and symptom information.

With the advent of real patients, our small pediatric faculty became very active, both in our fourth-floor clinic and our own fourth floor in the hospital, which was to be identified as the pediatric floor at the University for the next 50 years.

In addition, two young pediatricians, who had just completed their training at the University of Tennessee in Memphis, were beginning their practice in Lexington. Dr. James Wilhite had taken an additional year of child development in Memphis, and Dr. James Rackley had taken an additional year in hematology. They were spending part of their time in our clinics while starting their private practices in town. When their practices became busy, they spent less and less time with us. Dr. Rackley eventually became a medical missionary to Africa.

The rest of 1962 was spent enlarging our patient base without any local patients, in deference to the pediatricians practicing in Lexington. On July 1, we welcomed our first two pediatric residents, both of them through the Intern Matching Program, a minor coup for a brand-new department:

Roger Spalter, M.D.—University of Colorado, Denver

John Tyson, M.D.—Temple University, Philadelphia

Githens added Ann Presley, M.D., who was training in the Department of Community Medicine and needed experience in direct patient care. In addition, he was able to recruit Mike Sly, M.D., a senior resident from Cardinal Glennon Children's Hospital in St. Louis, to serve as our chief resident before going on to a post-doctoral fellowship in Pediatric Allergy.

With this housestaff, we were "good-to-go" for the coming year (July 1, 1962), although only four pediatric beds were available to us until mid-year. Our regular and our outreach clinics did provide much-needed clinical exposure for our trainees. Enthusiastically, we moved forward, excited to be a part of this pioneering venture.

Dr. Chart Mabry and June Robertson pinpoint the location of a young patient in far eastern Kentucky.

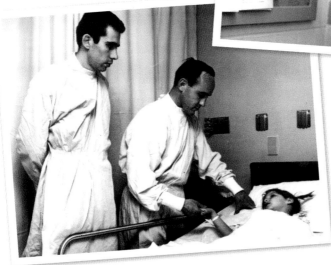

Dr. Mabry and resident physician making morning rounds.

CHAPTER 3

Claiming the Fourth Floor

As 1962 progressed, we began to have a few more patients, always from outside of Lexington, where we still were not infringing on the private practices of Lexington pediatricians. In July of 1962, we had an addition to our faculty, John Boehm, M.D. John had completed his pediatric residency and had a year of post-graduate training under Donough O'Brien, a metabolic specialist at the University of Colorado, who ran a microchemistry laboratory; this was to prepare him to care for prematurely born babies. Though Dr. Githens was very forward-thinking, I don't think he ever imagined how neonatology would develop.

During the summer we moved from the two semi-private rooms on 5 West to the fourth floor of the hospital, first occupying the East wing. This relieved pressure for pediatric hospital beds. Our first serious problem was a walk-in croup room with a mist machine that took up most of a whole room—the first room on the right on the East wing. It was an engineering marvel which administrators showed to all, but when we tried to use it, there were unanticipated problems. It required a lot of time and energy to crank it up and keep it working, and anyone who went in—patients, family, nurses, doctors—came out soaking wet. After the first week or so it was obvious that it was an inappropriate engineering monstrosity and was never used again. Eventually, all of the equipment (refrigeration, fans, and cabinetry) was removed.

We thought we were very fortunate in staffing our wing of the hospital. Ruth Pittman, an experienced social worker, was hired and was a joy to work with. She didn't try to move mountains, but became a trusted friend of our patients and their parents. She occupied a very small office on the ward, and I noticed that there was always a small bud vase with a fresh flower on her desk. The depth of her understanding of our patients was obvious in the typed notes that she put in the records. Ruth also facilitated family stays at a nearby motel, usually the Yocum Motel across the street from the Medical Center.

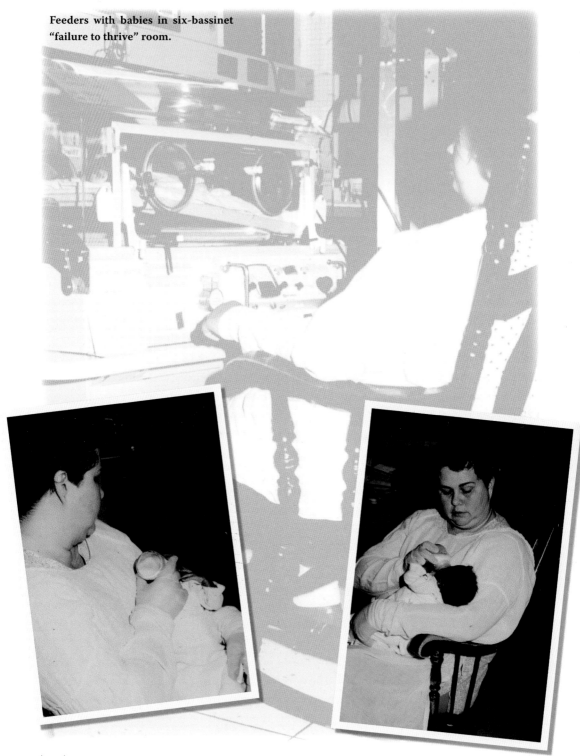

Feeders with babies in six-bassinet "failure to thrive" room.

The other significant staff member was Mrs. Virginia Aspy, RN, who was our first head nurse. Her enthusiasm and competence were helpful to all—physicians, other nurses, and the patients. She was always upbeat and had a can-do attitude.

For teaching and conferences, we used a single classroom on the ward just behind the nurse's station, where there were telephones and records. This classroom was used for the next couple of years as the room for our twice-weekly morning reports, our every-Thursday-morning grand rounds, as well as impromptu meetings and conferences throughout the week. It was in this room that each and every patient was vetted during morning reports and other meetings. Some of the local and out-of-town pediatricians began to attend these conferences.

Something that we had not expected was the numbers of visitors and how long they stayed. I realized early on that hospitals needed to relax some of the rigid visitation rules. I remember graphically a fellow medical student of mine in 1952 whose wife was found to have a persistent patent ductus arteriosus. He and his family decided that the best place to go was where they found the surgeon with the most experience with this problem, Boston Children's Hospital. The hospital did not allow visitors. Herb told me about sitting on the fire escape outside his wife's hospital room as his only way to visit. He spent many hours and a number of days on the fire escape talking and signaling to his wife on the other side. Obviously, something needed to be handled better.

Then, too, during my Philadelphia training, I had been a consultant for endocrine problems at the Shriners' Hospital for Children. The chief surgeon was Dr. John Royal Moore whose policy and, in turn, that of the hospital was to admit the patients and bid the parents farewell with no visitation allowed; then the child's clothes were burned in the hospital incinerator. It was a very sterile environment.

These experiences convinced me that parents, at least, needed to be with their children—but the entire family? When our first patients were admitted, it seemed that the whole family came with them. There were no provisions for parents and family to stay overnight, so they began bringing blankets and quilts and sleeping on the floor in the waiting room near the fourth-floor hospital rooms. At night a family member, usually the mother, would actually bed down on the floor under a crib or beside a hospital bed. We had made no provisions for couches or cots. Also, we learned that if we needed to speak with someone in the family, and they were not at the bedside or in the waiting room, we could probably find them in the parking lot sleeping in their pick-up truck or $200 car. They could be easily identified since Kentucky license plates have always carried the county name. We still have multiple family members come with their children for clinic visits or hospitalizations.

The traveling clinics were increasing in frequency, particularly since the opening of the Bert Combs Mountain Parkway had made it somewhat easier to travel to distant

Eastern Kentucky counties. One of my earliest memories is after a day-long general pediatrics clinic at the Health Department in Clay County, Manchester, when a health nurse, Ruby Parker, RN, took my wife and me on a Jeep ride to an outlying area in Clay County, Grannie's Branch. In the late afternoon we started up Grannie's Branch, driving up the creek bed because there was no road. Approximately 100 families lived on this one-mile branch of Goose Creek. You could see the shanty houses on either side of the creek, each with a straight pipe coming out to the creek, which drained their sinks. They did not have inside toilets; rather, they all had outhouses which, we hoped, did not directly drain into Grannie's Branch. As we progressed up the branch, we encountered two automobiles coming down the branch, driving coal miners with their hats and lights already turned on, going to the evening shift of a deep coal mine nearby. I don't remember how they got by us. It was really eye-opening to me to be next to the edge of the creek bed eye-to-eye with a chicken or a big hound—several times.

The poverty of these children was heart-rending. During this time, the general pediatric clinics were taking place twice a month in a different county health department; almost all of our doctors attended this clinic on a rotation basis. Dr. Noonan worked separately in parallel heart clinics, usually where there were both adults and children. Back at the hospital we were all taking turns as general pediatric attending in addition to our subspecialty patients. We had to be triple threats (teaching, patient care, and research).

All the while, we were establishing regular clinics in the clinic wing of the hospital on the fourth floor. They were beginning to pick up in numbers of patients. I remember so vividly on November 22, 1963, in the afternoon, when the assassination of Pres. John F. Kennedy happened and was played out on the television in the clinic waiting room. The clinic had to keep going, but we were constantly out looking at the TV to check on the progress of the situation. Grief, incredulity, and doomsday feelings prevailed.

We were quickly expanding our fourth-floor occupancy to fill the entire south wing and west wing. However, there had to be restraint on admissions because of an ongoing nursing shortage. At this point, the first of January 1963, Mrs. Aspy sent out an appeal for volunteers to help with the care of the children on the ward. I use the word "ward" because there was a six-crib unit on the East wing where the babies and small children were bedded down. A couple of faculty wives responded. The remembrances of one faculty wife (mine) follows:

>< ><

Burley

He was a morsel of a child. It took some minutes to figure him out.

I looked down at a small being with a baby's body and a three-year-old's head. It was January 1962, and the nurse, Mrs. Aspy, told me, "Burley will be three in April." I leaned over the crib's railing and said, "Hi, Burley, I'm Barbara. I have three little boys—and a girl (all of whom I had left with a neighbor girl). Would you like to come for a walk with me?" He observed me without interest. I held my arms out; he stared and then turned away. So I reached down and lifted him into my arms. He was soft and compliant, and he had a good bit of trouble supporting his large head. So we took the first of many walks over the next few weeks. At first he was completely silent and uninterested. But it didn't take long for him to relax into my arms, and I talked to him constantly—asked him questions and showed him things. He began to look where I pointed.

Burley was born on April 11, 1960 in Clay County, weighing between 7 and 8 pounds. He was never an eager eater and was said by relatives to have been "puny all his life." He seemed to have no interest in eating, and his mother, who soon got pregnant again, was not really much concerned with any of her children, who just got by the best they could. The mother reportedly roamed the streets most of the day. So, at the time of admission, Burley, at 2 9/12 weighed just under 13 pounds. And I was sure most of that weight was his head—a normal size, with a wide-open fontanel. He was suffering from malnutrition and neglect, from a horrible infestation of worms, growth and developmental retardation, anemia, and possible fibrocystic disease, bronchopneumonia, and a missing or non-functioning left kidney. His parents said he had sat up at one year and talked at two years; there was no sign of either at this point.

First, they got rid of the worms, and he stopped vomiting. They treated the pneumonia and the anemia and were trying hard to get him to eat. I arrived during the first week, when he was still flaccid and uncaring. The nurses and I tried to stimulate him, cuddle and rock—and feed him. There were several nurses at that point and only a few children. So we did a lot of walking and looking, Burley and I, and playing patty-cake and peek-a-boo. Within a couple of weeks I could tell he was enjoying himself a little, and he was supporting his head better. He leaned his big head into my chest, and together we discovered his feet. I brought an entire wardrobe of infant-boy clothes that my youngest had outgrown a few months before, and he really looked dressed up; I thought maybe he showed a little pride in his new clothes. He began to play with the baby toys I brought from home—not much, but some.

The biggest thrill—pure joy—was the day I leaned over his crib and he held up his arms for me to take him. And he smiled at me! I carried him around to all the nurses to tell them. He seemed to be proud, too. He began to eat without much protest, though he still did not want to hold his own bottle. So we took things slowly. My own children at home seemed to me to be walking, talking, wrestling miracles.

Burley ended up staying two months because they just couldn't bear to release him home to his incompetent, uncaring mother, so they invited his grandmother to come on several occasions over the second month and taught her how to take care of this fragile child. As Burley gained weight, he began to seem more like a toddler than an infant, though he was a long way from walking. He would accept some pureed foods but did not try to feed himself. He was not much interested in a cup. He liked his reliable old bottle.

Now he would look at books with me, but he didn't point or repeat the words. He did smile, and his eyes would light up when one of us leaned over to pick him up. He learned to sit when placed and to pick up toys, but sometimes he was withdrawn, too. He didn't seem to have much interest in his grandmother when she came but was docile when she picked him up. In fact, he was almost always docile. He basked in the attention, but seldom demanded it. We were getting very attached to Burley and hated to think about his going home. He weighed over 17 pounds at discharge, and his still-tiny body was filled out somewhat. He would stroke his little round belly appreciatively and smile up at us. I think I remember that he walked around his crib rails before he left, but I am not positive. It was a blue day for us when the grandmother came to collect him and his clothes and toys—and all the instructions. Burley had been one of the first patients admitted to the fourth floor pediatric ward, when there were only half a dozen patients, and each got plenty of attention—perfect for this child.

When he returned to clinic the next month, however, he had lost ¾ of a pound; the next month he had gained back a few ounces, and by the third month he weighed 18 pounds 9 ounces, and, by the next, 19 pounds 6 ounces. But apparently he never became a thriving or robust child. On a clinic visit when he was nearly 8 years old, he weighed slightly over 37 pounds, well below the third percentile. The public health nurses in Clay County were worried about him and asked to have him seen. We suspect that Burley was suffering from neglect and malnutrition. His sweat chlorides, measuring around 49, were below the cut-off of 80 at that time but above the current cut-off of 40. But, nearly 50 years later, I still remember that little morsel of a boy whom I watched become animated and responsive—and, yes, a little fatter.

Barbara Mabry, Volunteer

With great effort, I was able to locate Burley 46 years after his two-month hospitalization in 1963. He was never again a patient at University Hospital, and no one at the Clay County Health Department remembered him, nor could they find his records. I called three Burley ------s listed in the Clay County telephone directory—wrong person each time. Finally, he was tracked down through his disability payments—his check was cashed each month. He proved to be living in the same location as he had in 1963!

When I talked with his brother/guardian, three years his junior, the rest of the story came out during a late night, hour-long telephone conversation. When Burley was discharged to his father and paternal grandmother in 1963, they came to the realization that his very young mother had been neglecting and starving Burley. He cried and was fearful of her every time she got close; she was more devoted to her own parents and siblings than to her new husband and child. She had been giving most of the food that her coal-miner husband had been bringing home to her own parents and relatives. Figuring out what had been happening, Burley's father "discharged" Burley's mother.

Eventually, Burley's father took another woman, his second "wife," and with her had several more children. But Burley had been permanently damaged—an example of both maternal. emotional and caloric deprivation. Later he was enrolled in Head Start at Manchester Grade School and placed in the special education pathway. Years later, at the age of 20, he was graduated from the eighth grade with ceremony.

When his father was dying, he made Burley's younger brother, Robert, promise to take care of him. Robert has kept that promise, and Burley lives with Robert and his wife in a trailer on Samples Branch Road up a hollow. Robert manages Burley's monthly disability check, and life goes on.

❖❖❖

In February 1963, Jack Githens very quietly made the rounds to our offices and announced his resignation as Chairman and told us that he was leaving to return to Denver. His explanation was that it depressed him to be in Kentucky where there were very few sunny days. He compared the number of sunny days in Colorado to the number

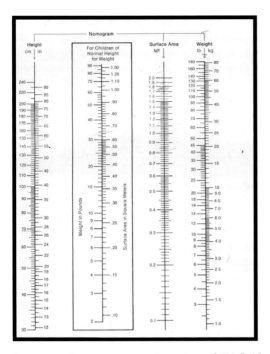

Square meter nomogram at center of IV-fluid controversy.

of sunny days in Kentucky. I thought this was a crock. Had he said that he could just not handle living in the Bible Belt culture of Kentucky, I would have understood. When asked about it years later, he said, "I decided then that I didn't want to be an administrator." Others close to Jack have said that seeing the plight of Eastern Kentucky children was just more than he could handle. Many of the stereotypes were true.

Meanwhile, we enjoyed professional collegiality, with healthy debate. One real issue with our faculty at this time was how we were going to do and teach parenteral fluid therapy. Those of us who trained on the East coast were dedicated to using the classical approach, based on weight of the patient and type of dehydration. You first calculated deficit therapy, then maintenance therapy, then

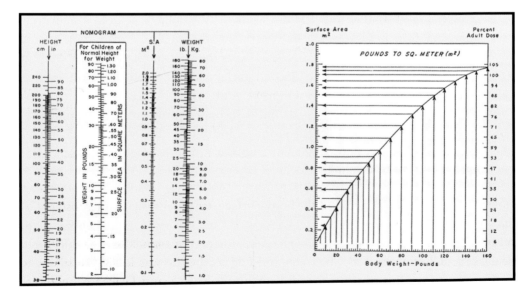

Alternative nomogram information for body surface area.

expected ongoing losses. This required that you modify fluids from various stock fluids and carefully monitor the patient's response over hours and days. Those who trained in the Midwest and West preferred using the new body-surface-area estimate and pre-stocked solutions. Moreover, they claimed that body surface area was "more scientific."

Story of the One-legged Man

I went to the library and found that doctors and scientists had been trying to determine body surface area for centuries. The first guess seems to have been made by Leeuwenhoek in 1719. He made his estimate based on the number of "little pores" in a square of skin. The effort to determine body surface area continued for the next three centuries, considering that fluid requirements correlated with metabolism rates and would be determined by body surface area rather than by weight. The methods used included covering the body with pieces of paper, then measuring the pieces of paper with a planimeter; skinning a cadaver and then measuring the stretched parts on a table; strips of tape; tin foil coating; and other novel techniques. There was significant experimental error in all the methods.

However, the greatest error was the selection of subjects measured. In the classic report by Du Bois and Du Bois in 1915 (12 subjects), several had missing legs, withered extremities from a stroke, tall and thin, fat, malformed from rickets, cretin, sculptor's model – no true normals. Oliver and co-workers summed it up that it was not so scientific in their classic paper from the Department of Pediatrics, University of Michigan Medical School.

FOOTNOTE: Oliver WJ, Graham BD, Wilson JL: Lack of scientific validity of body surface area as a basis for parenteral fluid dosage, JAMA 167: 1211-1218, 1958.

Come on, guys, body surface area is more scientific than weight and previously published adjustments for age? But the body-surface-area usage was further fostered by Clark West, M.D., a nephrologist from Cincinnati Children's Hospital, when he taught and published his body-surface nomogram, and our body-surface faculty continued to use Clark's nomogram and the body-weight faculty continued to use body weight. Like religion, you can only rarely change faith with knowledge.

✂✂✂

After Jack announced his resignation, the Dean quickly formed a search committee, headed by Bob Straus, Ph.D., Department of Behavioral Medicine. Already we had a bias of behavioral pediatricians on our small faculty, and Dr. Straus again began looking for a senior pediatrician who had an emphasis on behavioral medicine. But why behavioral? The first recruit, Bob Haggerty, was an outstanding person with those credentials. However, he was getting several offers and went on to his next stop, the University of Rochester, where he took their job. As the weeks marched on, the search committee made no communication with our very junior faculty. I remember so clearly when Bill Hathaway and I took it upon ourselves to visit with one of the search committee members, Harold Rosenbaum, the Chairman of Radiology. We told him that we were very young pediatricians and that we would greatly prefer an experienced clinician as our new boss. Moreover, we suggested Dr. Warren Wheeler, Professor of Pediatrics at Ohio State, based at Columbus Children's Hospital. We were familiar with Dr. Wheeler and his situation because he, the year before, had been fired as the editor of the American Journal of Diseases of Children, the specialty journal for pediatrics run by the American Medical Association. His offense had been that he refused to pull an editorial written by Dr. Lawson Wilkins about the corrupting of our journals by pharmaceutical companies' advertising. It would take some years until the medical community would be careful about the effect of pharmaceutical advertising. Now the companies are banned from providing lunches or gifts on the UK campus or to UK doctors.

In addition, Wheeler had been a strong candidate for the chairmanship at Ohio State, Columbus Children's, but had been passed over for a much younger candidate, Grant Morrow, a biochemical geneticist from the University of Arizona whom I had known as a postdoctoral fellow in Philadelphia. They moved the search committee forward and, indeed, Dr. Wheeler was selected.

When Warren Wheeler arrived on July 1, 1963, he took the position on the parenteral fluid therapy debate that "you can use any fluid that you want—as long as it is 'black Ford.'" This was derived from Henry Ford's assertion that you can buy a Ford in any color you want, as long as it was black. In Dr. Wheeler's mind, "black Ford" fluid was half-strength saline with 20 mEq KCl/liter with volume based on body surface area. From this position, you have to recognize that if the kidneys are still working, they can select what they need and dump the rest—they are "smart." Thus, the saying "he's got kidneys"—i.e., he's smart!

CHAPTER 4

Signature Patients

Three of the young original pediatric faculty were to discover and report sets of their patients very early in their appointments. These reports became their signatures in the medical world and served to let medical academia know that Kentucky was now on the national medical map. Moreover, all three investigators have continued to be experts on their respective subjects and have continued to study, report, and speak on their subjects:

- Bill Hathaway: Fletcher coagulation factor, a factor in the coagulation cascade.
- Jackie Noonan: Noonan syndrome, a malformation syndrome associated with pulmonic stenosis of the heart.
- Chart Mabry: Maternal phenylketonuria (PKU), a preventable cause of mental retardation in the genetically normal offspring of PKU-affected mothers.

OMIM 22900 FLETCHER FACTOR DEFICIENCY (PREKALLIKREIN DEFICIENCY)

Hathaway et al. (1965) described a Kentucky kindred in which four siblings by the name Fletcher showed a previously undescribed coagulation defect. Although they had no abnormal bleeding tendency, their blood showed much prolonged activated partial thromboplastin time and delayed thromboplastin generation but normal prothrombin time. Plasmas deficient in factors VIII, IX, XI, and XII corrected the abnormality.

Dr. Hathaway was recently (2007) designated the Hemophilia and Thrombosis Research Society Lifetime Achievement Award Winner. The unpolished story of how this coagulation factor was discovered is told by Bill Hathaway:

> During the time of establishing my first coagulation laboratory in John Githens' Pediatric Department at the new University of Kentucky Medical Center, a pediatrician, Dr. Joan Rider, in Lexington, called

to ask about a prolonged whole blood clotting time performed prior to tonsillectomy in an 11-year-old girl with a negative bleeding history. The child was in the midst of her first-ever pediatric evaluation after having been brought to Lexington for convalescent care for frostbitten feet. The patient, B., one of 11 children of an impoverished family named Fletcher, had walked barefoot from a burned-out cabin in the snow-covered hills of Eastern Kentucky (January 1963). The episode was considered particularly newsworthy since it occurred during Lyndon Johnson's "war on poverty." This remarkable series of events led to the performance on her plasma of Rapaport's activated kaolin partial thromboplastin time (APTT), a new test we had just set up in the laboratory. The strikingly abnormal results which corrected on prolonged incubation with kaolin stimulated

Hathaway's patients with coagulation factor deficiency standing at edge of family tobacco patch.

Drs. Bill and Sue Hathaway take blood from Fletcher family for study.

further investigations and convinced my research assistants and me that we had preliminary evidence for a new clotting factor which we tentatively designated "Fletcher Factor."

Initial contact with the father was arranged through a local health department in Salyersville, Kentucky. We met in the rain on the courthouse steps with a lot of bystanders and set up the next visit with the remainder of the family near a tobacco field for initial blood procurement (see Figures on page 46). Family studies frequently involved walking trips into the hollows of Eastern Kentucky. These efforts helped establish rapport with family members who remained cooperative when their "expenses" were paid. From the beginning of our studies, it appeared that the "Fletcher Factor" was part of the contact system of the coagulation cascade and perhaps represented the "missing" contact factor predicted by Schiffman, Rapaport, and others (1). In contrast, in a presentation given at ASH, Oscar Ratnoff, while introducing me, whispered that I had discovered a new "inhibitor." Although the Fletchers moved to Michigan and were "lost to followup" for a while, we continued to study the relationship of the new factor to factors XI and XII (2). In 1970, the second group of individuals with Fletcher factor deficiency was reported by Hattersley and Hayse (3). Although there were hints previously that the contact system was related to the kinin system, it was not until 1973 that these systems were closely entwined. The observation (4) that the Fletcher factor was the same as plasma prekallikrein was made by Kirk Wuepper, a dermatologist from the University of Oregon, working in Charles Cochrane's lab at Scripp's Institute in La Jolla, California.

The clinical significance of prekallikrein deficiency in man was then addressed by Wuepper, myself, and others by a study of two siblings of the original family. These studies and subsequent clinical observations indicate that severe plasma prekallikrein deficiency is not associated with any significant impairment in hemostasis, inflammatory responses, or leucocyte function (5). Since individuals with the genetic defect do not exhibit a bleeding tendency, a major clinical problem has been recognition of the cause of the prolonged APTT. As first demonstrated in 1993 (6), homozygotes with Fletcher factor deficiency show correction of the greatly prolonged APTT after 10-minute incubation (other than the usual 3 minutes) of their plasma with kaolin or celite while homozygotes with factor XII or high molecular weight kininogen deficiency do not correct. Fletcher factor heterozygotes do not have prolonged APTTs since their plasma contains adequate levels of prekallikrein for normal activation.

OMIM 16395 NOONAN SYNDROME

In 1968, Jacqueline Noonan reported 19 cases, of whom 17 had primary pulmonary stenosis and two had patent ductus arteriosus—12 were males and seven were females. Deformity of the sternum with premature closure of sutures was a frequent feature. Recently, a mutation in the PTPN11 gene has been present in about 50% of affected individuals, and the phenotype is wider than previously described.

Jackie Noonan writes for us the inside story of the discovery and implications of her findings:

> *When I finished my pediatric cardiology training in Boston on June 30, 1957, I went to Iowa City to begin an pediatric cardiology program. This was not unusual in those days since there were few pediatric cardiologists in medical schools throughout the country. During my stay at Boston, I was pretty discouraged by the high mortality of children undergoing heart surgery and I felt that it would be better if we could find out what caused heart disease so that perhaps we could prevent these cardiac lesions. I had noticed during my pediatric cardiology training that children with congenital heart disease often had other associated non-cardiac anomalies and some of them seemed to have a number of anomalies that would fit into a syndrome. For this reason, I thought it would be important to study some new patients that I would see at Iowa and to see if I could come up with something that might help us understand better the etiology of congenital heart disease.*
>
> *With that in mind I went to Iowa, where I began a little clinical study. Dr. Dorothy Emke was a pediatric resident at Iowa, serving half-time as chief resident and half-time as my fellow. Together we began to study every new patient. This was before computers, so all our data were collected on little 5 x 7 cards. We reported such things as birth weight, the history of the pregnancy, whether the mother had any illnesses such as rubella, whether she had diabetes, whether the baby was a twin. We asked a lot*

about family history and we recorded not only the congenital heart defect but also the other anomalies that were present. We finally collected about 833 such patients before I left Iowa to go to Kentucky to be part of the faculty at this new medical school.

It became apparent to me fairly soon in this study that there were nine children who looked remarkably alike. They looked like brothers and sisters. They had dysmorphic facies consisting of low-set posteriorly rotated ears, some hypertelorism, down-slanting palpebral fissures, ptosis, and a short neck. The children in general were short in stature. They often had a chest deformity. What was of great interest was that all of them had pulmonary stenosis, some mild and some quite severe. In addition, several had, in addition to pulmonary stenosis, an atrial septal defect. These patients I thought represented a new distinct syndrome. The girls had some resemblance to Turner's syndrome and I suspect a number of the patients reported in the literature as Turner's syndrome were really patients which we now call Noonan's syndrome. Because Turner's syndrome had a sex chromosome abnormality, when they were males it looked a little bit like Turner's syndrome. The term "male Turner" came into vogue. The endocrinologists looked hard to find a problem with the Y chromosome but none was found, and it turns out that the patients called male Turner probably consisted of a number of different syndromes, but clearly some of these male Turners turn out now to be what we call Noonan's syndrome. I was fortunate that Iowa City under Dr. Zellweger had developed a chromosome lab and we were able to study the first female we saw and could determine that she did not have Turner's syndrome since she had a normal 46XX chromosome count. I left Iowa City and came to Lexington. I had submitted an abstract to the

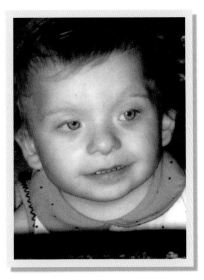

Young girl with Noonan syndrome consisting of short stature, dysmorphic facies with low-set posteriorly rotated ears, hyperteliorism, down-slanting palpeteral fissures, ptosis, short neck, and cardiac pulmonic stenosis.

Midwestern Society for Pediatric Research and this meeting was held in 1962. I presented my paper at that meeting and it was of interest that many people discussed this, what I had called, "a new syndrome."

By chance, Dr. John Opitz, who has become quite a famous geneticist, was a resident in Pediatrics at Iowa City when I went there as a new faculty member. He was interested in genetics and I had the opportunity to teach him and talk to him about some of these patients with a variety of syndromes who had congenital heart disease. He laughed because I would say, "You see that child who looks like that? He probably has pulmonary stenosis." So John was really quite surprised that a pediatric cardiologist could diagnose the kind of heart disease a patient had just by looking. Of course, this was just lucky that I was able to predict the heart disease, but clearly pulmonic stenosis was common enough in this condition that it was really a pretty good guess. In any event, John Opitz left Iowa and went up to Madison, Wis., and trained with Dr. David Smith, a very well known dysmorphologist. While he was there, he began seeing patients and called them, "There's a girl with Noonan's syndrome." And they would say to him, "Why do you call it Noonan's syndrome?" And he said, "That's what Dr. Noonan taught me." But then John said, "You know, Jackie, it's hard to call this syndrome Noonan's syndrome when Noonan hasn't published on it". Well, by that time I had been in Lexington for a while and had found 10 additional patients who looked just like the patients in Iowa City.

All nineteen of these patients had some form of congenital heart disease; 17 had pulmonic stenosis of varying degrees, varying from mild to very severe, while two had isolated patent ductus arteriosis.

This paper was published as a new syndrome with associated congenital heart disease in the American Journal of Diseases of Children in October 1968. The title of the paper was "Hypertelorism with Turner Phenotype" but across the top of each page was the term "Noonan's Syndrome." This was largely due the efforts of John Opitz. John convinced the editor of the Journal, Dr. Ashley Weech, who happened to have been my chief when I was a resident in Cincinnati Children's Hospital, that it was appropriate to name this syndrome Noonan's syndrome. He felt that I was the first one to recognize that this condition occurred in both males and females, that it could be inherited, that the chromosomes were normal, and that they had congenital heart disease. In any event, the term "Noonan's syndrome" became official when Dr. Victor McKusick put it in his Dictionary of Mendelian Genetic Syndromes. It's been a great delight to me to have this syndrome named in my honor, and I have maintained a very active interest in the syndrome and have published extensively since that time.

In the late 90's, just about the time I retired, so to speak, from the department, I got a phone call from a mother who stated that her daughter had just been diagnosed with Noonan's syndrome and none of the doctors knew anything about it. She wanted to know where there was a Noonan's syndrome support group. I told her that I thought there was one in California but I'd never heard from them, but I did know there was one in London, England, that Dr. Michael Patton had been involved in. Well, this woman found out about the support group in England but decided it wasn't exactly the kind of support group she had in mind. She therefore started her own group and about a year later I got a phone call from her saying, "We're going to have our first international Noonan's syndrome support group," and asked if I could come. Unfortunately, I had another commitment and could not go, but since that time I have attended every Noonan's syndrome support group meeting and these have been held now in several parts of the world. I was in Belgium this past two years attending a Noonan's syndrome support group in Belgium. It is actually run by the mothers of patients with Noonan syndrome who want to know all that the doctors know about Noonan syndrome. Wanda Robinson, who started this group, is able to attract physicians who are interested in Noonan syndrome from all parts of the country to come at their own expense to participate in the conference. The children are brought along, so it's a family affair. It is really very exciting and rewarding to see these children with Noonan's syndrome, some of whom have never seen another child like themselves, who immediately bond and have a great time playing and getting to know each other. The teenagers are already texting and certainly using their cell phones and computers to stay in touch. As I *tell the Noonan syndrome people at this meeting, I learn more from them than I certainly teach them at these yearly conferences.*

OMIM 261600 PHENYLKETONURIA (PKU)

Phenylketonuria is significant because it was the first known cause of mental retardation treatable by dietary means. Features other than mental retardation include a "mousy" odor, light pigmentation, peculiarities of gait, stance, and sitting posture, eczema, and epilepsy. The basic defect stance in PKU is phenylalanine hydroxylase deficiency. Heterogeneity in PKU is due to multiple alleles of the gene or defects in its coenzymes. Fetal damage from maternal PKU can be prevented by dietary therapy for the affected mother if it begins before conception. The occurrence of mental retardation in the offspring of homozygous mothers is an example of a genetic disease based on the genotype of the mother. The damage is aggravated by the normal placental process, which functions to maintain higher levels of amino acids in the fetus than in the mother. We were surprised by these findings, for it had been assumed that PKU females did not procreate—but they do, even in the worst of circumstances.

The story of how these PKU mothers were discovered is told by this author:

> *In November 1962, Dr. Joe Denniston called the department's front office to see if anyone could measure blood phenylalanine for him. Measurement of blood phenylalanine was not generally available, and the only commercial laboratory measuring blood phenylalanine was BioScience in California—expensive and requiring 10 mL blood to do the Kapler-Adler method. Joe had been the pediatrician at the Hazard Kentucky Miners' Hospital until he had a massive heart attack. After a period of convalescence, he had to take the less demanding job of superintendent at Clover Bottom Hospital and School just outside Nashville, Tenn. In this 1,000-bed facility, all the inmates had an administrative record, but not a medical record. When he arrived at Clover Bottom, he set out to create a medical record on each patient: a medical history, physical exam, CBC and urinalysis, to include a ferric chloride test. As he got started, he encountered our index family (Page 54). Conveniently, I had just developed a method for measuring blood phenylalanine using only 0.1 mL serum!*
>
> *Later in the month, I went to Clover Bottom and stayed over for two days. In touring the hospital, I observed a marble "car wash" for patients*

strapped to their gurney—parked in marble slots—Dr. Denniston had shut this down. The patients were in all states of disability, many in cribs or beds secured with over-bed nets. Clover Bottom, the former site of President Andrew Jackson's estate, was much like our own Frankfort State Hospital and School and Pennhurst in Pennsylvania where Nobel Prize winner Pearl Buck had refused to place her child, later found to have PKU.

Mabel's story

This PKU mother's story began in West Point in northern Mississippi, where she was one of several children born to a cotton sharecropper's wife. As a young woman, she took up with a local young man destined to be a house painter, and they moved to Memphis, Tenn., where he continued to paint houses and became an alcoholic. When he died, local authorities placed Mabel, the mother, and her five children in the Shelby County (Tenn.) Poorhouse. County "poorhouses" were in every county across the South, a place to put people who could not care for themselves or their children.

It is significant that Mabel's IQ was higher than all five of her children's IQs; she had PKU and they did not. Over the years, Mabel's children were transferred to Clover Bottom where they resided as typical mentally retarded patients. In time, as the current disability system began operating, Shelby County Court decided to shut down its poorhouse. What to do with Mabel? Since all her children were at Clover Bottom, they sent her there to be with them. Her oldest child, Lilly Mae, died at Clover Bottom, and her youngest son had been released back into the general population. When we tracked him down, he was driving a truck in Nashville.

Finding a maternal PKU case that led to publication fired up Joe, and he became an enthusiastic promoter of the care of mentally retarded patients. Shortly after our publication, he became the superintendent of the Sand Springs, Oklahoma, Hospital and School for the Retarded, which led us to three more maternal PKU families; however, these mothers were functioning in open society, but their retarded children were living in the institution. In all, we had assembled seven cases over a short period of time.

To assess more thoroughly the incidence and the morbidity of maternal PKU, Harvey Levy undertook an international survey regarding the frequency and morbidity

MATERNAL PHENYLKETONURIA*

A Cause of Mental Retardation in Children without the Metabolic Defect

C. Charlton Mabry, M.D.,† Joseph C. Denniston, M.D.,‡ Thomas L. Nelson, M.D.,§ and Choon D. Son, M.D.¶

LEXINGTON, KENTUCKY, AND DONELSON, TENNESSEE

IT has been demonstrated that excessive phenylalanine, or its products, can damage the developing brain of an otherwise normal young animal or human infant, and clinical studies suggest that the phenylketonuric infant's neurologic damage is acquired. There have been no animal experiments concerning the effect of an abnormally elevated maternal serum phenylalanine level on a developing fetal brain. Furthermore, it is generally considered that persons with phenylketonuria seldom reproduce because of their severe mental retardation. Thus, there have been almost no observations on their offspring.

We have recently found 3 elderly phenylketonuric mothers who have had 1, 5 and 8 children respectively. All their living children have been examined and found to be mentally retarded, with neurologic deficits; however, they do not have phenylketonuria. These findings depart from the few published observations on phenylketonuric mothers and their children. A summary of our combined observations and studies on these families is reported.

REPORT OF MOTHERS AND THEIR CHILDREN

Family 1 (Fig. 1 and 2)

Mother, H-II-10, proband: this elderly institutionalized woman, born in 1890, was recently found to have phenylketonuria during an institution-wide urine ferric chloride screening program. Although little is known about her childhood development, she was said to have been a "nervous and shaky," blue-eyed, flaxen-haired child. She had attended elementary school for a few years, and sometime during her early teens had begun working in a factory as an unskilled worker. At the age of 22 years she married an elderly man who had had 4 normal children by 3 previous marriages. An older sister recently stated, "had father been alive, he never would have allowed it"; this statement, along with others, indicates that the family did not consider her wholly normal. She had 5 children (III-9, 10, 11, 12, 13) and was doing well, until the depression of 1930. At that time she and all 5 children were placed in a county poorhouse. She remained there until the death of her husband in 1940, when she was transferred to Clover Bottom Hospital and School, where she has remained along with her children and where she is ambulatory and socially adapted, and is assigned chores. On examination she has no gross abnormalities and appears in good health. She has gray hair, blue eyes and the general findings of advanced age. She has never had eczema or seizures. Generalized hyperreflexia and bilateral Babinski reflexes were present. An electroencephalo-

*From the Department of Pediatrics, University of Kentucky Medical Center, Clover Bottom Hospital and School and Sonoma State Hospital (a preliminary report of a portion of these families has been made[1,2]).

†Instructor in pediatrics, University of Kentucky School of Medicine.

‡Superintendent, Clover Bottom Hospital and School, Donelson, Tennessee.

§Associate professor of pediatrics, University of Kentucky School of Medicine; formerly, superintendent, Sonoma State Hospital, Eldridge, California.

¶Staff pediatrician, Clover Bottom Hospital and School, Donelson, Tennessee.

gram and liver-function tests were within normal limits. On psychologic testing she was assigned an overall I.Q. of 49. Special laboratory studies are summarized in Table 1.

First child, H-III-9: this child, born in 1918, died in 1940 with acute gastroenteritis and thus was not available for examination. A review of her records revealed that she was admitted to Clover Bottom Hospital and School in 1931, and at that time she was a small girl who had just begun to have normal pubertal changes. It was stated that "all reflexes are hyperactive." On intelligence testing in 1936 she was functioning at a 5-year-old level (I.Q., 30).

Second child, H-III-10: in 1931 this brunette woman, born in 1920, was transferred from the poorhouse to the Clover Bottom Hospital and School, where she has continued to reside. At the time of admission she was obviously retarded, and, on psychologic testing in 1955 and 1962, she was assigned an I.Q. of 32 and 33, respectively. She is ambulatory, cares for her own personal needs and is sometimes assigned simple chores. On examination she appeared grossly normal except for a defect in articulation causing partially mutilated speech. Her reflexes were normal. An electroencephalogram and liver-function tests were within normal limits. Special laboratory studies are summarized in Table 1.

Third child, H-III-11: this brunette woman, born in 1922, was also transferred to this institution in 1931 and has continued to reside there. At the time of admission she was obviously retarded, and, on psychologic testing in 1950, 1956 and 1962, her I.Q. was between 27 and 30. She is ambulatory, cares for her own personal needs and can do simple chores. Usually, she is docile, but does lose her temper and become combative on occasion. On examination there were no gross abnormalities except for slight speech impairment. She had generalized hyperreflexia. An electroencephalogram was normal, and liver-function studies negative. Special laboratory studies are summarized in Table 1.

Fourth child, H-III-12: this blue-eyed, dark-haired man was born in 1924 and appeared normal during early childhood. His mental slowness did not become apparent until late childhood, and thus he was not transferred to the Clover Bottom Hospital and School with his sisters. He was transferred in 1939 and has continued to reside in the

FIGURE 1. *Family 1: Patients H-III-10, H-II-10 (mother), H-III-11 and H-III-12.*

Reprinted from the *New England Journal of Medicine*
269:1404-1408 (December 26), 1963

Index family of first report of the maternal PKU sequence. Retarded mother in dotted dress with more retarded non-PKU older children around her. Mabry et al. reported six additional similarly affected families, a previously unrecognized cause of mental retardation in non-PKU offspring. *Reprinted with permission of The New England Journal of Medicine.*

associated with maternal PKU. It showed that the injury to the fetus correlated with the degree of hyperphenylalanemia in the mother.

Now that females with PKU are entering motherhood with increasing frequency and many have become non-compliant to strict dietary treatment, we are at a crossroad of increased disabilities and morbidity in the PKU population—they are genetically normal but deliver damaged fetuses. I have great hopes of avoiding this crisis by treating PKU patients with the newly available cofactor, synthetic tetrahydrobiopterin (Kuvan®). Many of our patients on Kuvan are keeping their blood phenylalanine within the treatment range of 1-6 mg/dL, and some have seen significant diet relief.

These "signature" cases demonstrate that placing a new medical school on the edge of Central Appalachia, perhaps the poorest and least-educated region in the country, need not condemn their faculty to professional exile. Moreover, having a national presence has steered many new faculty and housestaff in our direction. Since our department was established in 1960, there have been eight more medical schools and two schools of osteopathy started in nearby states, all with Departments of Pediatrics—none of which has a national presence. To further increase our national presence, I suggest we place a greater emphasis on research, present at important national meetings, and push our advanced care initiatives.

References Fletcher Factor

1. Hathaway WE, Belhasen IP, and Hathaway HS: Evidence for a new plasma thromboplastin factor. I. Case report, coagulation studies, and physiochemical properties. Blood 26:521-532, 1965.

    The original paper citing the Fletcher Factor was a Citation Classic in Current Contents edited by Eugene Garfield.

2. Schiffman S, Rapaport SI, Ware AG, Mehl JW: Separation of plasma thromboplastin antecedent (PTA) and Hageman factor (HF) from human plasma. Proc Soc Exp Biol Med 105:453-454, 1960.

3. Hathaway WE, Alsever J: The relationship of "Fletcher factor" to factors XI and XII. Br J Haematol 18:161-169, 1970.

4. Hattersley PE, Hayse D: Fletcher factor deficiency. A report of three unrelated cases. Br J Haematol 18:411-416, 1970.

5. Wuepper KD: Prekallikrein deficiency in man. J Exp Med: 138:1345-1355, 1973.

6. Hathaway WE, Wuepper KD, Weston WL, Humbert JR, Rivers RPA, Genton E, August CS, Montgomery RR, Mass MF: Clinical and physiologic studies of two siblings with prekallikrein (Fletcher factor) deficiency. Am J Med 60:654-664, 1976.

References Noonan Syndrome

Noonan JA: Hypertelorism with Turner phenotype: A new syndrome with associated congenital heart disease. Am J Dis Child 116:373-380, 1968.

Noonan JA: Noonan syndrome and related disorders. Progress in Pediatric Cardiology 20:177-185, 2005.

References Maternal PKU

Mabry CC, Denniston JC, Nelson TL, Sun CD: Maternal phenylketonuria, a cause of mental retardation in children without the metabolic defect. N Eng J Med 269:1404-1408, 1963.

Mabry CC, Denniston JC, Coldwell JG: Mental retardation in children of phenylketonuric mothers. N Eng J Med 275:1331-1336,1966.

Mabry CC: Maternal phenylketonuria; clinical overview and review of the literature. Proceedings of Fourteenth General Medical Conference, Collaborative Study for the Treatment of Children with Phenylketonuria. Stateline, NV, March 13-16, 1978.

Lenke, R.R., Levy, H.L.: Maternal phenylketonuria and hyperphenylalanemia; International survey of treated and untreated pregnancies. N Eng J Med 303: 1202-1208, 1980.

Mabry CC, Karam EA: Measurement of free amino acids in plasma and serum by high voltage paper electrophoresis. Am J Clin Path 42:421-430, 1964.

McCaman MW, Robins E: Fluometric method for determination of phenylalanine in serum. J Lab and Clin Med 59:885-890, 1962.

CHAPTER 5

Change

D r. Warren E. Wheeler, a professor of Pediatrics from Ohio State University, Columbus Children's Hospital, arrived, as the administration planned, on July 1, 1963, promptly at 8 a.m. for the routine morning report. Dr. Wheeler, always with his pipe, took his seat in the room behind the nursing station near the window on the first row, a perch he kept for the next 11 years. As morning cases were presented, he made pertinent comments, and we heard the first of a long series of Wheelerisms. On this occasion, when the diagnosis was being questioned, he remarked "when you hear hoofbeats coming down the road, you think of horses, not zebras." Many more similar aphorisms were to follow over the years. My favorite was "everyone talks about hobby horse manure, but no one ever sees it." On the wards, I remember this one's being dropped frequently on work rounds in the morning. Dr. Wheeler would interrupt a medical student in mid-presentation to ask "how many medications is the patient on?" If the answer was more than two, he would reply, "This is the doctor's problem." The message to be transmitted to the housestaff was obvious, and they moved on to the next bed. I wonder what he would say today?

Dr. Wheeler's routine was quickly established. Every day at 7:30 a.m. he went to the clinical bacteriology laboratory, where Colonel Tucker, the head of that section, had laid out pertinent Petri plates showing cultures taken from the previous day(s). After inspection and consultation with Colonel Tucker, he would proceed to morning report, or Grand Rounds,

Warren E. Wheeler, M.D.
Harvard 1933
Chairman 1963-1974

and take his front-row seat. Dr. Wheeler was obviously very comfortable and happy in his role looking over the shoulders of students, housestaff, and faculty as they worked with their patients, providing the needed stability for a very young faculty. As patient-care supervisor, he could be counted on to be present either in his office or on the wards all day Monday through Friday and until noon on Saturday. He never sat down in one of the several research laboratories to chat. Warren Wheeler's interests were general pediatrics and infectious diseases. His practice and vision were within the walls of the hospital.

Not surprisingly, after Dr. Wheeler's arrival, Githens' recruits, except for Mabry and Noonan, had left within two years to go to other institutions. That faculty was steadily replaced, mostly by informal recruiting and mostly by former residents under Dr. Wheeler, or by wives of other medical school faculty who were certified in pediatrics. As they arrived, they are listed below.

Joyce Gryboski, M.D.—Yale University Medical School, Yale University (gastroenterology)

Phillip Holland, M.D.—Louisville Medical School, Cincinnati Children's Hospital (hematology)

Nancy Hinkle Holland, M.D.—Louisville School of Medicine, Cincinnati Children's Hospital (nephrology)

Doane A. Fischer, M.D.—Temple University School of Medicine, staff pediatrician, Harlan, Ky., Miners Hospital (academic/general pediatrics)

Robert Beargie, M.D.—Ohio State College of Medicine, Oklahoma Children's Hospital (premature/sick baby nursery)

Marina Yarbro, M.D.—Peru, University of Minnesota Children's Hospital (metabolism)

Robert Achtel, M.D.—Cincinnati College of Medicine, Yale University (cardiology)

Joseph Burke, M.D.—University of Kentucky Residency, Cincinnati Children's Hospital (gastroenterology)

David Wilson, M.D.—Southwestern Medical School, Dallas, St. Louis University (infectious diseases)

Dorothy R. Hollingsworth, M.D.—University of Virginia/Washington University St. Louis (adult endocrinology)

Vernon James, M.D.—Boston Children's Hospital medical school, University of North Carolina (developmental pediatrics)

Kenneth Gerson, M.D.—University of Montreal medical school, Ohio State University (allergy)

Dr. Wheeler, never called Warren, was "old school" and practiced within the walls of the institution, never involving himself in our outreach efforts and never changing during his 11 years at the helm. In this chapter, I want to honor Dr. Wheeler, but I also want to define him. He was a rock-ribbed Republican who didn't want to spend money, particularly tax money. I remember his telling us that at the end of his first year at Columbus Children's Hospital in 1945, the hospital superintendent called him into his office to discuss a financial crisis. The per diem cost for the year had risen from $6.43 per day to $6.87 per day. Since the per diem now at the University of Kentucky Hospital is about $1,000, he is probably turning over in his grave!

After Dr. Wheeler was here for about a year, some members of the pediatric faculty became concerned that our research was declining because we now were more focused on service and direct care of patients. So we introduced a Wednesday noon faculty conference in a small room where individuals could talk about what was going on in their research laboratories. We quickly ran out of things to discuss in this small weekly forum and began inviting clinical and laboratory researchers from other parts of the school and some outside speakers. The outside speaker who had such an eye-opening talk relevant to what we were doing in and for Eastern Kentucky was Harry Caudill. I had read the review of his book, *Night Comes to the Cumberlands*, in *Science* magazine; I phoned Mr. Caudill and invited him to speak to our group. He was very accommodating, especially since he was soon to accompany his wife, Anne, on a shopping trip to Lexington. They had always lived in Whitesburg, near the Virginia border. He graciously agreed to speak to us. We were all captivated by his talk and revelations of how Eastern Kentucky had become what it was. It was his book that spurred the national War on Poverty. He enjoyed his sack lunch and cold drink (Pepsi) that I had prepared along with my own before I left for the hospital. Pepsi was and still is the cold drink of choice in Eastern Kentucky—except maybe for Ale-8-One.

During the 1960s, our doctors and hospital were being heavily scrutinized by Kentuckians, especially by Eastern Kentuckians. Rumors circulated that they "experimented" on people at University Hospital. Our outreach clinic helped allay some of those fears. In the summer of 1966, Bob Beargie and I examined all the Head Start children in Owsley County at the health department in Booneville. After that long day, I walked across the road, Ky. 26, to the new office of Dr. Robert Adkins, a dentist. Bob had been in our first graduating UK Dental College class, indentured to work in rural

Kentucky. He told me of an adult patient he had had earlier in the week, Maddie, who had complained that a doctor with the children's traveling heart clinic in Hazard had told her that her eight-year-old daughter, Emma, had a "hole in her heart and needed to be fixed." Maddie had refused the surgery for Emma, saying, "That's the way God made her and that's the way she is going to stay!" Bob had countered with, "Maddie, what do you think God made heart surgeons for?" Immediately a light came on in Maddie's head! So the following week, Maddie went to the health department to see Nurse Ruby and asked her to call Dr. Noonan's office at the University. Later in the year, the hole in Emma's heart was closed. Slowly but steadily, suspicions about our hospital diminished and continue to dwindle.

Although day-to-day life continued relatively unchanged on the fourth floor, changes outside the department would quickly modify our small world. In the spring of 1963, University President Frank G. Dickey resigned. On May 31, 1963, Gov. Bert Combs, chairman of the UK Board of Trustees, named John W. Oswald, Ph.D., a 45-year-old Minneapolis native, as the sixth president of the University of Kentucky, effective Sept. 1, 1963. Dr. Oswald had been running the community college system in California. His arrival marked significant changes. First, he changed chairman appointments on main campus from lifetime to four years—and six years in the College of Medicine. There was a loud outcry on main campus, particularly from the lifetime appointees in History and Botany. In the College of Medicine, hardly anyone had an opinion. Next, he discontinued the state retirement plan for faculty and substituted the personal investment portable plan used throughout most educational institutions (TIAA/CREF). For this, the faculty remains grateful, especially considering the financial bind that the state retirement plan is now in.

As part of the shakeup, Dr. Oswald told our dean, Dr. Willard, that he would no longer have a direct budget pipeline to the governor or the General Assembly—rather, the Medical Center budget would henceforth be part of the whole budget request and go through him, the University president. This was more than Dr. Willard could tolerate, so he retired to an Alabama catfish farm.

Pres. Lyndon B. Johnson visited East Kentucky on a tour of poverty-stricken Appalachia on April 24, 1964, kicking off the War on Poverty from the front porch of a battered tarpaper shack in Beauty (Lawrence County). The following spring, President Johnson signed into law the $1.4 billion federal-state program of economic aid for Appalachia, on March 9, 1965. These monies would allow for better access to health care for most Appalachians, particularly by building roads to allow them to get to Lexington and back home within a day. However helpful that was, some of our patients still have very long days.

Furthermore, this increased access for patients to University of Kentucky Medical Center would have a turn-around effect on our philosophy of medical education, our catchment area of responsibility, and the type of medical care provided.

As the patient load increased, there were rumblings from county judges throughout the area that some counties were being favored over others for medical care. Thus, an edict came out, rationing beds, with each county being given a number of admissions to University Hospital each month. For an attending and admitting physician, this was very difficult and obviously quickly broke down, for we saw severely sick patients by referral and could not readily determine whether their county had overused its allotment that month. Obviously, this was not a workable plan. Not long afterward, though, because of the new access to care through Medicaid for our patients, rules were handed down from Central Authority that the number of allotted days a patient could stay in the hospital was determined by a new scheme based on diagnosis (Diagnostic Related Groups, or DRGs), designed to reduce the number of patient days and, thus, the cost of care. This federal system simply didn't work. Next, the feds thought that an effective way to reduce the number of hospital days was to limit hospital days for deliveries, allowing mother and baby to stay in the hospital for only 24 hours unless they had a serious complication. Previously, we had been keeping babies and mothers in the hospital for several days. This ruling caused a national uproar and was abandoned, although there are still modified practices of this in the Medicare/Medicaid system.

The influx of new patients supported by Medicaid caused what many clinical faculty referred to as "clinical overload," which effectively reduced much of their research time and effort. Although there was much debate about this, I think that basic-science faculty were immune because they didn't see patients and were probably unaware of the stress going on in the hospital.

The challenge that clinical overload caused in the medical school also brought about a change in medical education philosophy. That philosophy originated in 1956, and included interdisciplinary teaching and the team approach—in practice taking more time and slowing the movement of patients from intake to discharge. For a university hospital to function as a demonstration hospital rather than a regional referral hospital was no longer tenable. The original goal of developing primary care physicians to return to their home counties was no longer tenable, either—most students just did not want to go back. Married students, especially with children, cited the poor quality of the school systems in their home counties.

All the while, Dr. Wheeler was following the party line and hiring faculty with little or no subspecialty training. Faculty appearance as speakers at national and regional clinical research meetings declined to zero during some years. Yet, we held on to the reputation of being a good place for general pediatrics training.

Changes began to occur at the top as deanships changed several times, leading to the present goal of becoming a top-twenty research medical school and no patient's (child) having to leave the state to receive the best of care. And no longer do we look to East Kentucky for our patients—our mantra is that now we bring advanced medical care to all. Our students and housestaff are immersed in all of this, seemingly confident that they can achieve these goals.

Dr. Wheeler did not participate in this change in medical education philosophy—he kept using his previously successful style of being a bedside scientist, responsible for all the patients on the fourth floor. There was a never-resolved dispute within pediatric surgery and pediatric neurology over Dr. Wheeler's position, "I'm in charge."

Meanwhile, exemplary clinical service was being provided to all patients, but there was a decided atrophy of research and interest in publishing. As mentioned, this situation led to our pediatric service's being regarded as a high-quality place to train a general pediatrician, but not appropriate for an academically oriented pediatrician. Nevertheless, the pediatric residents in this era all came to respect and honor Dr. Wheeler, who had on every occasion been an immediate backup for them.

During this decade, Dr. Wheeler brought the stability and respect from students and housestaff that we needed. In the first few years of his tenure, it was difficult to attract housestaff, but finally the department became recognized as a good training site if you wanted to go into practice. Later, still during the Wheeler era, three of our senior faculty had a meeting with Dr. Wheeler, complaining that we were not moving forward either on originality or research, nor was there a vision for the future. He really seemed not to understand the need for that aspect of our department. He responded by saying that if he could "find a five-year plan, he would dust it off and look at it."

We did, during the Wheeler era, have our first two postdoctoral Fellows, Arturo Bautista in Endocrinology and Metabolism and Carol Cottrill in Pediatric Cardiology. Dr. Bautista eventually returned to his native Bolivia, but, because of political problems, he re-emerged in Houston, Texas, where he was and still is a beloved practicing general pediatrician. Arturo Bautista was one of Dr. Bricker's first attendings in internship at Texas Children's Hospital in Houston and a lasting influence. The other Fellow, Carol Cottrill, trained under Dr. Noonan and is still on our faculty and an important contributor to our Cardiology Division.

During this period, we were very actively recruiting resident physicians. While I was the housestaff coordinator, I would get on the phone after receiving an application and arrange to meet candidates at the airport and take them to the motel we rented across the street from the hospital.

The Smilin' Mighty Jesus

In addition to adjusting to the wariness of the local pediatricians, there were also cultural accommodations.

One day, probably in the fall of 1963, an overalled grandfather came into the emergency room carrying a limp and feverish little girl with her head on his shoulder. He told the pediatric resident on duty that Dr. Paul Maddox sent him down. Residents were convinced from prior experience that patients sent to them were really sick, because he took care of almost everything himself, in his Campton Clinic.

The resident tried to take a history but got little information, and the grandfather, probably in his 60s, just kept shaking his head. "Don't know what you want," he declared: "Speak plain."

The resident, from New Jersey, got the child's age, where she was from, how long she had been sick, then tried to take the child to examine her. Her grandfather only reluctantly let him put her on the table.

"Doc says she has The Smilin' Mighty Jesus and that you will know what to do."

"The Smilin' Mighty Jesus," grandfather pronounced again. "What's the medicine for that?"

The resident continued an abbreviated examination and excused himself. "Bring somebody here that speaks the language," grandfather called after him.

The resident ran to find his colleagues, telling them that he needed help, he could not understand what Dr. Maddox, via the grandfather, had suspected.

New Jersey repeated "The Smilin' Mighty Jesus" two or three times; finally, one said, "High temp, stiff neck, sleepy?"

"Yes!"

"I would guess you might look for spinal meningitis," he said, grinning. "Want me to go with you to translate?"

Barbara Mabry

We also began to see some diversity in our housestaff. William Underwood, M.D., UK Pediatrics Resident 1966-67, tells the story from that point on:

I came back to UK (did my undergraduate work at UK) in July 1966 from Vanderbilt University to function with Chip Griffith, as Senior/ Co-Chief Residents. We had seven Pediatric house officers (Underwood,

Griffith, Tony Mansell, Sally Moore, Ingrid Daoud, Bailey Binford and Dave Keefe) and used rotating Interns.

Because of the small numbers of housestaff, we were very busy, with two house officers per night in the hospital and every third night duty, which seemed easy after two years of "on 36 hours/off 12 hours" at Vanderbilt. It was a great learning experience because of the dedicated faculty who worked as hard as the housestaff and saw that we learned at every opportunity. But we hesitated to call them at night unless it was life or death, so we learned from first-hand experience.

We did this for $500 a month, which again was a step up from Vanderbilt's $125 a month—so I guess it was the money that brought me here. It was a wonderful experience and prepared me for practice here in Lexington (Lexington Clinic 1967-98) and ultimately for my triumphant return to UK (1999-present) to help train another generation of UK pediatric housestaff.

Dr. Wheeler was willing to maintain the status quo and to criticize "the use of intrepid surgery," and he referred disparagingly to the "vogue for salvaging the unsalvageable (small pre-term babies)." But as the push to set up Neonatal Intensive Care Units (NICUs) escalated, he hired Robert Beargie, M.D., from Oklahoma Children's Hospital to come and set up a premature/sick baby nursery at Kentucky. At one point, Bob had 21 isolettes going in the old Premature/Sick Baby Nursery in a very small space, with cables and hoses crisscrossing the floor. Although the staff was hard-pressed to keep up, Dr. Wheeler never once visited that Premature/Sick Baby Nursery, nor did the hospital administrator during Bob's five-year tenure as head of this special nursery.

Meanwhile, as smaller and tinier (under 2 pounds) preemies were sent to University Hospital, Dr. Beargie had to deal with their new-to-us problems. One of the most vexing was apnea, no breathing for 20 seconds or more. Though apnea occurs frequently in preterm infants and is usually idiopathic and transient, in many instances it also is associated with an illness— central nervous system injury, an infection (especially respiratory), a pulmonary anatomic condition, a metabolic problem presenting as hypoglycemia or electrolyte disturbance, feeding or gastrointestinal

Robert Beargie, M.D.

problems or various cardiovascular conditions. A doctor or nurse could not stand by and observe every baby all at the same time.

To alert Beargie and his staff to a baby who had stopped breathing, he sought help in our Research Electronics Shop—one of the specialty shops in the hospital basement. There, he linked up with Peter Burbank, an electronics technologist hired in October 1966. Burbank had voluntarily left the U.S. Navy, serving the last several years on the first Polaris sub patrolling underwater north of the Arctic Circle off Norway. Not wanting to spend his life underwater, he surfaced at our Medical Center and was immediately hired to do whatever medical electronics work needed to be done. Burbank tells the story of building the first infant apnea monitor:

> *I set about putting together all the building blocks needed. The transducer or sensor was the key. It was a silicone rubber tube filled with graphite powder that, when stretched, provided a varying resistance. A metal contact plug was inserted at each end of the rubber tube, both to contain the graphite powder and to provide an electrical connection to be routed via a shielded cable to the signal processing and alarm unit. The sensor was also attached at each end to a Velcro waist strap to position the sensor on the infant. The maximum "breathing motion" signal was just below the infant's rib cage.*
>
> *This breathing signal was then amplified, turned into a square pulse, and sent to a timing/alarm circuit. The audible alarm was quite loud and since the control unit was usually placed on top of the isolette, the noise would often startle the infant awake or into a breathing state. Later, we hired a design engineer who had worked for several electronics firms including Union Switch and Signal (railroad crossing signals). His name was Irvine P. Stapp. He designed a Version II apnea monitor that drew less current from the battery. Battery supply was chosen because it entirely isolated the infant from all other adjacent electrical hazards, the enclosure accommodated the largest lantern battery, and it was immune to power outages.*
>
> P. Burbank

From start to finish, it took only two months to build. In addition to the prototype monitor, other monitors were built and placed in use. This was a shining moment in our nursery in 1966. Having the instrument patented was considered, but the design

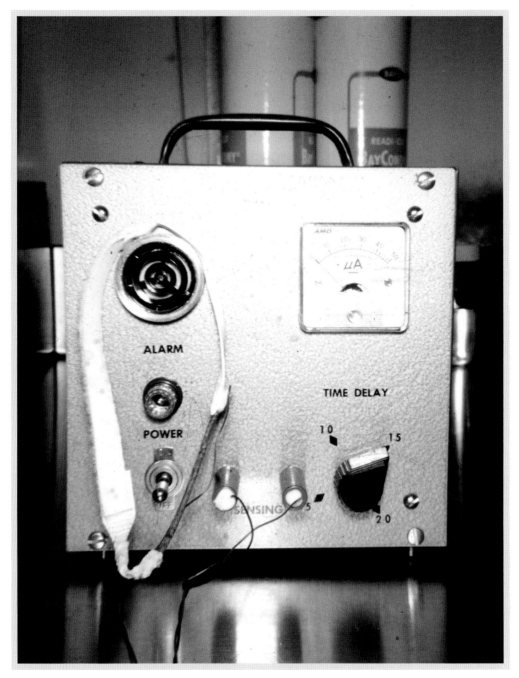

Prototype of Beargie-Burbank first American apnea monitor.

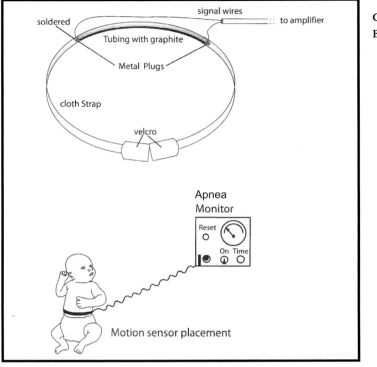

Components of the Beargie-Burbank apnea monitor.

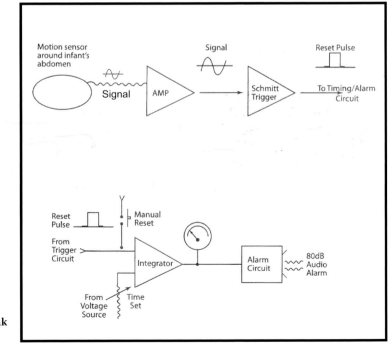

How the Beargie-Burbank apnea monitor worked.

engineer assigned to the task did not follow through; the University Law Office had little or no experience in securing a patent and was of no help.

Eventually, the University put the Beargie/Burbank infant apnea monitor "out for bid." Air Shields Corp. picked up the bid and made some modified monitors. I can't trace the marketing of the monitor beyond this point, but the commercial monitors now available differ somewhat from the Beargie/Burbank prototype. In 1975, Burbank's son's middle school class made a trip to Boston, Mass. The son became quite excited when he saw the prototype model atop an infant isolette with his father's name on it at a Harvard science museum.

Infant apnea monitors are now in general use in nurseries everywhere, and many infants wear them for weeks, even months, after they are discharged to home. Beargie, grandfathered into the Neonatology Board ranks, and Burbank now are retired—Beargie in Lexington and Burbank in Oklahoma.

The next generation of apnea monitors used stick-on electrodes and shot an RF (very low) current through the baby's diaphragm muscle to stimulate a breath. Current models use more advanced methods and equipment. So, this first apnea monitor methodology lasted less than a decade, illustrating the growing role and rapid changes of electronics in medicine.

By 1965, our medical student and housestaff numbers had greatly increased so that we did not have enough clinic patients or hospitalized patients to accommodate them for teaching. An arrangement was made for a local pediatrician, Dr. Abe Fosson, to leave his private practice at The Lexington Clinic and become a full-time pediatric faculty member stationed in the Baby Health Clinic of St. Joseph Hospital. There he supervised patient care in Baby Health Clinic and coordinated the teaching with the private pediatric and private pediatric surgery patients. Because even the private

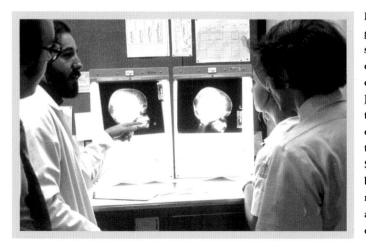

Dr. Abe Fosson mentoring a group of third-year medical students. They had just come from the bedside of a child with meningitis at St. Joseph Hospital. Part of the third-year medical students obtained experience under the umbrella of Baby Health Service patients off-site because of the limited number of pediatric patients at University Hospital and clinics 1970-1974.

pediatricians and the pediatric surgeon, Dr. Richard Segnitz, appreciated Abe's presence, it was a sought-after rotation for both students and housestaff. In 1976, all teaching was moved back to University Hospital and clinics. This foray into the private practice world further cemented the good relations between the private physicians and our faculty. Sick children were only rarely referred to Cincinnati or Louisville. Again, Baby Health had promoted pediatrics in our region.

Since not long after Dr. Wheeler arrived, he had become frustrated that we did not have microchemistries to serve and use with our patients. He had come from Columbus Children's Hospital where Sam Meites, a clinical chemist, had provided labor intensive manual microchemistries for all their patients. At the time, I had a connection with our Department of Pathology because its staff had assumed the use of my recently developed high-voltage paper electrophoresis methods for identifying and measuring amino acids, sugars, and other substances as a standard clinical laboratory offering. I thought that I could adapt the newly available Technicon® roller-pump continuous-flow system for chemistries that were being introduced in clinical laboratories throughout the country. I wanted to change the sample sizes of one to two ml to less than 0.1 ml. I

5.0 ml **0.5 ml** **2.0 ml**

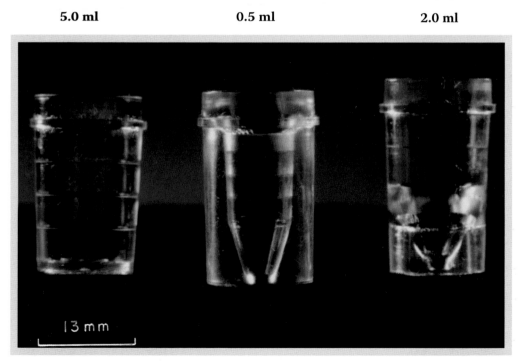

Specimen sample cup, maximum volume 0.5 ml, manufactured specifically for micro-automated chemistries. Previous sample cups contained 2.0 or 5.0 ml sample. The 0.5 ml sample cup was well suited for our systems, requiring only 0.05 to 0.10 sample volumes.

don't know where he got the money, but Dr. Wheeler bought me a train of Technicon® equipment for $7,000, a lot of money at that time. I began working in the chemistry division of the Central Clinical Laboratory and methodically converted their equipment and methods to reduce sample volume to 0.1 ml (instead of 1-3 ml then required). This micro-automation received wide interest at the time, and people began visiting to observe these new methods and systems. In an effort to cut down on sporadic visitors, we offered a postgraduate course in 1977; 132 clinical laboratory people, physicians and technicians, from New York to Los Angeles and Chicago to Miami visited, and our new systems were shown at the Annual Chicago Meeting of the American Society of Clinical Pathology. With this change, the number of tests on our patients rapidly increased so that a typical hospital patient had 20 to 30 tests performed on the same blood sample rather than the previous three to five tests. This greatly expedited the evaluation and care of our patients, but Dr. Wheeler was bothered that a lot of unrequested information

AUTOMATED CONTINUOUS FLOW ANALYSIS
The reagents used in standard manual methods are diluted appropriately and roller-pumped individually through tiny polyethylene tubes to mixing coils. From the coils, the reagents and serum/plasma/urine/CSF samples flow to separate sides of a long dialyzer membrane with the reagent side continuing to a colorimeter or flame photometer. The intensity of the color in the liquid or flame is continuously recorded. Bubbles separate the patient samples. The heights (peaks) of standards are manually compared to the peaks of individual patient specimens with final results reported. Approximately one patient specimen per minute is recorded.

MODULES AND SPECIMENS FLOW FROM RIGHT TO LEFT
The reason the modules and specimens flow from right to left is because that is how Leonard Skeggs, clinical chemist at the Cleveland, Ohio, Veterans' Affairs Hospital, built the original prototype on his home basement workbench. He cleared stuff off to the left as he worked over a period of months. His methods and modules were adopted by The Technicon Corp. outside of New York City, where they were manufactured and distributed across the nation in just a few years.

Skeggs, Jr LT: An automated method for colorimetric analysis, Am J Clin Path 28: 311-322, 1957.

Mabry CC, Roeckel IE, Gevedon, RE, Koepke JA: Recent advances in Pediatric Clinical Pathology, Grune and Stratton: New York, 1968, pp. 18-77.

Pump manifold examples

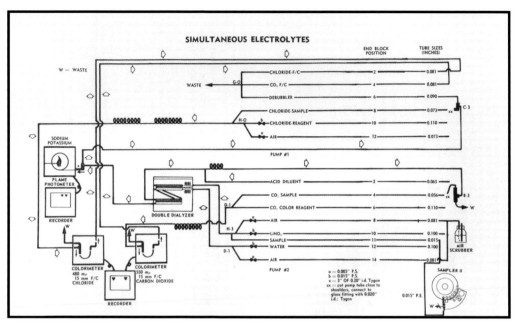

Auto analyzer pump manifold for electrolytes requiring 0.1 ml sample.

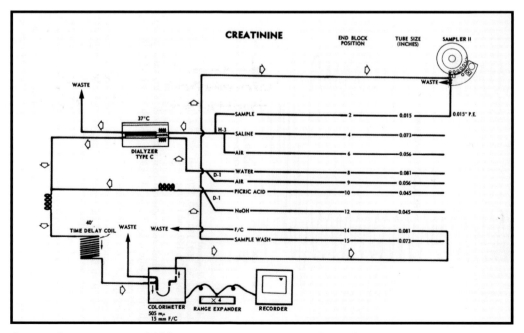

Auto analyzer pump manifold for creatinine requiring 0.1 ml sample.

Recording samples

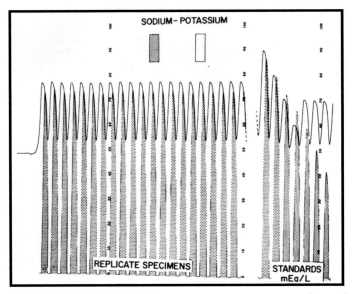

Sodium and potassium simultaneous specimen recording of standards and control.

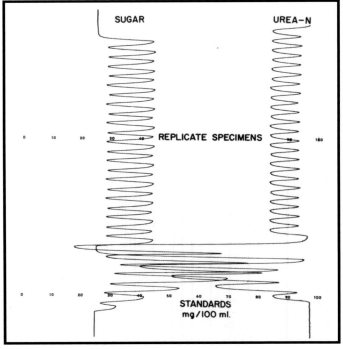

Sugar and urea nitrogen simultaneous recording of standards and control specimen.

Recording samples

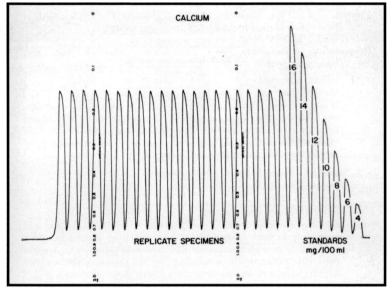

Total calcium standards and control specimen.

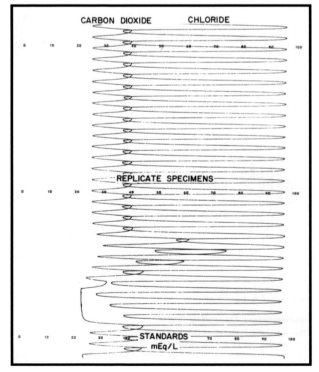

Total CO2 and chloride simultaneous recording of standards and control specimen.

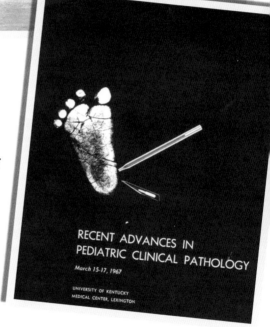

Group picture of doctors, laboratory technicians and instructors who attended March 15-17, 1967 workshop on automated microchemistries.

was being reported. This was when panels of test results began to be used.

When our first reports of automated microchemistries were made, we began to get requests to visit our laboratory. When we realized those visits were disrupting our regular work, we decided to hold a demonstration-workshop. We reported these new laboratory methods in a 345-page training manual—a still-useful book titled *Recent Advances in Pediatric Clinical Pathology*. UK held a three-day course March 15-17, 1967. One hundred and twenty-nine attendees—physicians, clinical chemists, and med techs—came from New York to California and from Florida to Canada. A group photo from the front of the Medical Center is shown above. The public elementary school and football field shown in the background have been replaced by the College of Nursing building and Kentucky Clinic.

In the foreword of our monograph, Dr. Wheeler and Dr. Pete Stewart elucidated why our new methods were important:

> *The University of Kentucky was fortunate to have the authors of this book on its staff. Dedicated to the idea that children are more important*

than anybody, and that somehow we ought to be nice to them and protect them from painful and frightening experiences when they are sick, these workers came up with the logical solution—use methods designed for children for everybody! ...

The authors are well qualified to have accomplished this simple solution. Dr. Mabry, for instance, is a pediatrician by training, a chemist-pediatrician whose investigative work lies in the area of metabolic diseases, inborn errors of metabolism, and genetics. Many of the analytic methods in his type of research laboratory require the smallest of samples. As a clinician dealing with remote mountain families with children having PKU, he needed a way for mothers to draw blood samples and mail them to the University to monitor the dietary management of their children. So he devised a method to suit his requirements. He was one of the early American workers to exploit the potentialities of high-voltage electrophoresis. Brought up in the research laboratory, he is devoted to accuracy rather than expediency.

Warren E. Wheeler, M.D.
Professor and Chairman
Department of Pediatrics
University of Kentucky
Director of Pediatric Service
University of Kentucky Hospital

... due to restrictions in space, personnel, and funds, it is nearly impractical for a clinical laboratory in an active general hospital to provide different methods of performing clinical laboratory examinations for children and adults. The obvious solution has been found, namely: adapting all the methods to small samples suitable to children. This the authors have accomplished almost entirely through their own efforts, but with some early assistance from members of the Technicon Corporation. Basically, what they have done is modify, occasionally extensively, methods used in the routine chemistry laboratory so that no single determination or group of determinations requires more than one-tenth of a milliliter of

serum. The accuracy and precision of these methods has been carefully explored over the years and there is reason to believe they are actually superior to the standard methods ... .

Through the efforts of these individuals and all other personnel in the laboratory, we have been able to provide more than satisfactory service for the children and at the same time improve our services to adults. This illustrates the advances possible in patient care when there exists close collaboration and interchange of information between the laboratory and clinical services.

W. B. Stewart, M.D.
Professor and Chairman
Department of Pathology
University of Kentucky
Director of Laboratory Services
University of Kentucky Hospital

References Automated Microchemistries:

Mabry CC, Gevedon RE, Roeckel IE, Gochman N: Automated submicrochemistries; a system of rapid submicrochemical analysis for the measurement of sodium, potassium, chloride, carbon dioxide, sugar, urea-nitrogen, total and direct-reacting bilirubin and total protein. Am J Clin Path, 1966, 46:265-281.

Mabry CC, Warth PW: An automated technique for separate fluorometric measurement of epinephrine and norepinephrine in urine. Am J Clin Path, 1969, 52:57-68.

Mabry CC, Roeckel IE, Koepke JA, Gevedon RE: Recent Advances in Pediatric Clinical Pathology. New York/London, Grune and Stratton, 1968.

Mabry CC, Warth P: Micro-automated parallel measurement of serum calcium and phosphorus. Am J Clin Path, 1967, 37: 395-400.

Faculty, housestaff, head nurse and play lady after Grand Rounds, June 1964 (private practitioners in suits). Front row: Robert Warfield, M.D., opened a pediatric office in 1935 in the pediatric ghetto on Second Street. Warfield wrote Dr. Richard Elliott's obituary for the Fayette County Medical Society record. Second row, left: Carl Scott, M.D., was the first pediatrician not to practice in the Second Street pediatric ghetto. His office was on Nicholasville Road. Second row, right: Richard Segnitz, M.D., was Lexington's first pediatric surgeon. He operated at St. Joseph Hospital, never at University Hospital. He was active in the Department of Pediatrics teaching program.

Meanwhile, the clinical faculty and staff was busy caring for children and teaching medical students and residents. In medicine, you have to do it to teach it. Some of the faculty and staff are pictured above.

These micro-automated methods remained in daily use in our Central Clinical Laboratory for about 10 years, being replaced by mechanical robot chemistry methods also using micro sample volumes of plasma, serum, CSF, or urine. Again, a show of the rapid changes in technologies and methods in medicine.

Meanwhile, changes were occurring on the national level—progress, real progress.

Declaring the War on Poverty, President Johnson in 1965 introduced both Medicare and Medicaid, providing financial access to health care for many individuals in both far Eastern Kentucky and in the small farm districts in and around Central Kentucky. The practical result for us was that many more patients began coming to our hospital for services, thus very quickly causing a clinical overload. In spite of our need for expansion in the number of beds, we were unable to staff more hospital beds because of nursing and allied health worker shortages. Dr. Wheeler, along with Robert Straus, chair of Behavioral Medicine, conceived of the idea of a Care-By-Parent wing, the 4 North Wing. Helpful in many ways, Care-By-Parent gave a place for parents to stay alongside their infant or child, and we had some very novel uses. This arrangement stayed in place for about 10 years, until the crush for conventional beds increased.

Also accompanying the War on Poverty was a greater emphasis on our traveling clinics, so that general pediatrics expanded from one to two per month; the pediatric cardiology clinic expanded as well. Another new development was the establishment and funding of Head Start programs in every school district in the state. A problem with those in Eastern Kentucky was that they had no physicians who were able to take on the extra responsibility of even examining these five-year-old children, most of whom had never had a routine doctor's visit. Indeed, many had never seen a doctor, since they had been delivered by midwives.

A call for help from several school districts came to our department, so several of us began taking a couple of weeks of vacation to work these clinics during the summer. Helped by the local health nurses, Bob Beargie and I did this in several counties for several summers. For me it was very revealing as to what the true health status of Kentucky was. Also, discovering certain patients during these clinics, on at least two occasions, led to significant publications on my part and were career-advancing. I continue to see

Dr. Wheeler's first housestaff at University Hospital. Garner Robinson, M.D., chief resident, seated. In Sook Chung, M.D., with her new baby.

those patients sometimes in our Lexington clinic, and others have also studied the same patients who have come out of these hollows. One summer my wife accompanied Dr. Beargie and me for several days. On a hot afternoon (at Jones Fork Elementary School) in Knott County, when school buses were being held so we could finish the Head Start exams, my wife witnessed the following, which she recorded as a poem:

THE LEONARD STORY
All the mothers in their long cotton dresses
and with their younger kids had gathered to witness
 their children's first-ever examination,
by the Head Start doctor from the University –
 a big event in this mountain community in the sixties.
They sat crowded in a semi-circle in folding chairs
 around the edge of the un-airconditioned classroom,
juggling fretful younger children but watching—
 watching every move the doctor made
and commenting quietly among themselves.
 The children were laid on the teacher's desk
wearing only their much-washed underwear,
 or, if they had none, a towel over their hips.
They were silent and big-eyed—a little scared,
 but the young doctor was gentle and reassuring
as he listened to their chests and palpated tummies.
 Then the big infant who came to be known as Leonard,
hot, restless, and too-long restrained,
 began to squall and squirm.
The large mama unbuttoned, whipped out
 an udder-sized breast and tried to stuff it
into the child's furious mouth.
 He flailed and resisted, grew more red-faced
and violent and screamed even louder.
 Though the exams continued without pause,
the other mothers, sticky and tired,
 shuffling their heavy shoes, were getting restless too.

The sweating mama tried harder to cram it in—
    too slippery now to get a good hold on.
Finally she yelled in total exasperation:
    "Leonard. Leonard, if you don't take your dinner,
    I'm going to give it to the doctor."
Leonard finally latched on, hiccupping;
    there was a collective sigh in the steamy room,
and the red-faced doctor applied his stethoscope
    with sweat-slick hands, hiding a bit of a quiver,
relaxed his shoulders, thankful not to need to turn around
    and wondering if he could still manage
to give out the worm-pills.

                                   Barbara Mabry

As we worked our way through our daytime assignments to examine both five-year-olds to be entered in the Head Start Program and also six-year-olds, examined by a physician for the first time, it dawned on us that we were seeing younger siblings who were behind in development. We later realized that, coincidentally, they had been born in the fall or winter. After investigating, Dr. Beargie prepared a description of, and explanation for, this "winter baby syndrome."

In spring, not infrequently, an Eastern Kentucky youngster presents to our clinic facilities with the "Winter Baby Syndrome." This child is brought to clinic at 18 to 20 months of age because he doesn't walk yet. Sitting and crawling have also been delayed.

If you keep the winter baby in mind, it is easy to recognize his rather typical history. He is born during the winter months. His home is heated by a coal or wood stove. The wood floor of the home is raised from the ground level and is sometimes covered with linoleum. The floor is cold in the winter except very close to the stove. This child spends most of his waking and all of his sleeping hours on a soft thick mattress in a "six-year crib," which is placed near the heat source in the cold weather.

On examination, you find he prefers to lie on his back and hold his flabby lower extremities in flexion. His upper extremities, he uses well. Social and language development are normal.

It is quite clear now that these children who are born during the winter are too young to be placed on the floor or out in the yard during their first summer. As they go into the cold months, the crib is placed near the heating stove, incidentally, usually the center of family activity. During his second winter, when he is approximately one year of age, the child is kept off the cold floor. Being restricted to the limits of a soft mattress, he is unable to gain firm purchase necessary for early sitting, crawling, or standing. Parents and siblings provide adequate, sometimes abundant, stimulation for language and social development. Gross and fine motor skills of the upper extremities are usually well acquired due to the sibling play over the crib rail.

During that second winter, if he were not previously a back-sleeper, he now assumes the supine position to enjoy better the family activity around him. If he were a congenital back-sleeper, severe occipital flattening and protuberance of the ears become the hallmark of the winter baby.

Treatment consists of explanation, reassurance, and suggestion. The youngster will walk within four to six weeks of the time he is put on the floor or out in the yard. The winter baby becomes a summer walker.

So there were tangential benefits for these children, including treatment of worms.

During one of his exploratory trips, Jack Githens, soon after his appointment, was visiting all the pediatricians he could find in Central and East Kentucky, and he discovered Doane Fischer at the Harlan Miners' Memorial Hospital (MMH). He had known Doane when they were in medical school at Temple University in Philadelphia. Doane had joined the Harlan MMH in 1955, becoming the leading pediatrician in Southeast Kentucky, where he was comfortably in charge.

Since Jack's first visit to Harlan, there had been a dramatic downturn for patients in the Miners Hospitals. In the autumn of 1962, the United Mine Workers of America abandoned the region. And in September, the union overlords suddenly began canceling the membership and welfare cards of miners whose employers were in arrears with payments to their

Doane Fischer, M.D.

welfare fund. The affected miners were numbed by the letters that told them they had been expelled from the union they had fought to build.

On Oct. 12, 1962, the trustees of the welfare fund announced that four of its twelve hospitals would be permanently closed. The Presbyterian Board of Missions came to the rescue and assisted in establishing the Appalachian Regional Hospitals. A number of physicians who elected to remain in Harlan founded the Daniel Boone Clinic, which is still in operation—but times were tough. Moreover, the clinic used the new UK Medical Center for patient consultation and care. Doane developed an active relationship with our department. When Dean Jordan came on board in 1969, there was a new emphasis on preparing primary care doctors, a new designation for general practice that included pediatricians, internists, and obstetricians. When Doane became interested in moving to Lexington, Dean Jordan hired him to head up the Division of General Pediatrics, where he served from 1969 until his retirement in 1984.

Not long before Doane Fischer died in 2007, he wrote this early history of the Division of General Pediatrics:

<h3 style="text-align:center">General Pediatric Clinic
1969 to 1974</h3>

When the College of Medicine had opened, Dr. Pellegrino had recruited two general practioners, Dr. Joseph Hamburg and Dr. Nicholas Pisacano. Dr. Willard had been supportive of this but it never did fly. When Dr. Jordan became dean, he hired Dr. Irving Kanner in Internal Medicine and me (Doane Fischer) in Pediatrics.

This was the first time full-time faculty were appointed to these two positions. Earlier, two pediatricians had been responsible for General Pediatrics: Dr. Chamberlain, who also had Behavioral Pediatrics as his prime interest, and later Dr. Vernon James, who was also responsible for developing the Child Development Program. During that period the other members of the pediatric department contributed time to the general clinic, but there was no full time presence and no dedicated space. When I arrived, all Pediatric Clinics were held in half of the fourth-floor clinic in the original ambulatory wing. (Now Surgical Offices.) At the beginning, the department was completely on one floor, with offices, labs, hospital ward, clinic and premature nursery all within short walking distance of one another. Not long after Dr. Wheeler's arrival, the much acclaimed Care-By-Parent unit was opened on 4 North. Also, more importantly, the Kentucky legislature was pushing for more preparation of primary-care physicians.

In the fourth-floor clinic space the second corridor was occupied by Pediatric Ophthalmology and Pediatric Dentistry. This provided easy access to consultations in the two disciplines. In Dentistry Dr. John Mink, the chairman of Pediatric Dentistry, and Dr. Herbert Sorenson were readily available. Dr. Jonathan Wirtshafter and Dr. Richard Keeler were the ophthalmologists. A teaching lab, which we regularly used, and a conference room were also on this corridor.

At first, General Peds clinic examining rooms were moved from available location to available location. Then a specific area was designated, as students and housestaff were spending more time in the clinic. On their required pediatric block, juniors all spent some time in the clinic, attending several of the specialty clinics as well as General Peds. Two teaching sessions were held each day. In the morning we had "place reading contests" when Dr. Wheeler reviewed strep screening cultures, and we reviewed cases from the previous day. At noon we had a daily conference on selected general ambulatory conditions. Every morning the faculty and housestaff went to "Morning Report," where Dr. Wheeler led the discussions of recently admitted patients. As patient numbers increased, the clinic conference room was converted to a walk-in clinic, and later a night clinic was started. On Friday mornings General Pediatrics had all the clinic examining rooms for a very large well-baby clinic. On other days of the week several of Lexington's practicing pediatricians were co-attendings, but on Fridays we could usually expect four to six pediatricians to come and teach. Regulars included Dr. Jody Rider and Dr. Noble Macfarlane. We also had regular help from several pediatricians from farther away: Drs. Bob McCloud and Pat Jasper from Somerset and Dr. Guy Cunningham from Ashland. There was no problem of who charged for what, and we had a great mix of attendings. We learned from one another.

Not long after I arrived, Dr. Abe Fosson joined the faculty, commissioned to develop an inpatient resident rotation at St. Joseph Hospital. On occasion I covered for Abe, and the residents and I were joined by Dr. Richard Segnitz, a pediatric surgeon, for lively joint rounds. As new faculty, Abe and I attended many informative conferences on teaching techniques that were funded with the Federal Capitation Grants of that time. We developed teaching-slide programs and installed study cubicles for the junior and senior students. The division assumed responsibility for the Junior pediatric curriculum, and we experimented with different teaching and evaluation methods. Next, a senior elective was developed in the clinic.

Besides running the clinic at UK, the division assumed responsibility for running the regional pediatric clinics in several Eastern Kentucky counties. The most frequently visited counties were McCreary, Magoffin, Wolfe, and Clay counties. A resident and a junior student would join us at 5:30 a.m. to head off for an enlightening day in the mountains.

Originally, Dr. Earl Vastbinder (an adolescent pediatrician) ran a clinic at the Juvenile Detention Center on Cisco Road in Lexington, but as he got more involved in training Physicians' Assistants in the College of Allied Health, General Peds took responsibility for the Detention Center. Shortly after we assumed responsibility for the Detention Center, the city opened a day-care center for abused and neglected children, and we began a clinic there in the building near the Detention Center.

General Pediatric faculty numbers slowly increased. From a one-man show with help from specialty faculty, from practicing pediatricians, and from the chief resident, we expanded one individual at a time. Dr. Betty Wolff, who also worked in child development, added her expertise to the clinic. Dr. Priscilla Lynn, who had been a fellow in the old premature nursery, joined as a full-time attending. After completing her chief residency, Dr. Jackie Campbell became the third full-time person. They were joined or followed by Dr. Claudia McEwen and Dr. Danny Fermaglich.

Dr. Dorothy Hollingsworth (the wife of the Chairman of Internal Medicine) joined Dr. Mabry in endocrinology. Her major activity was developing the YPP (Young Parents Program), which was held in the Pediatric Clinic, with physician support from General Pediatrics. When WIC (the federal Women, Infants, and Children nutrition-assistance program for low-income families) was initiated in Kentucky in 1972, a WIC worker was sent from the Health Department to this clinic.

Child psychiatry provided in-clinic consultation. First, Dr. Robert Aug came on a regular basis. When Dr. Otto Kaak arrived, he took over the weekly clinic consultation position, providing a great teaching resource. In addition to their working with the Child Development

Program, two clinical psychologists were available to the clinic to provide testing and counseling. First, we had Dr. Marilyn Marks and later Dr. William Meegan.

During those early years, with everything moving at a slower, more collegial pace, it was convenient for teaching and for patient care to have available a number of very responsive specialists from other departments: Dr. Horace Norrell in Neurosurgery, Dr. Tom Brower in Orthopedics, Dr. Robert Belin and later Dr. Andy Pulito in Pediatric Surgery. There was no ENT department for a number of years, and we had a real need for someone to evaluate and treat our patients with serious ear infections. Dr. Walter Harris, a volunteer faculty member, agreed to come one day a week to see these children. When the pediatric neurologist in the department left, Dr. David Clark, a world-famous neurologist, became Chief of Neurology as a separate department. He insisted on being responsible for pediatric neurology, and he and Dr. Wheeler had some very difficult negotiations over who would care for CNS infectious diseases. Dr. Albert Selke was the pediatric radiologist, a valuable resource for evaluating x-rays. From the College of Pharmacy, Dean Joseph Swintowsky placed a full-time Pharm.D in the clinic to fill prescriptions and educate patients, but, when his grant ran out, he had to leave.

All of the division members began having private patient days, and when the third clinic facility was opened in the early 90s, space was developed for two pediatricians to see UK-HMO patients fulltime. One of the early practitioners was Dr. Mark Parrott. This third clinic is the present department facility, and in the mid to late 80s or early 90s, the division was assigned two full pods plus other space so that the space crunch was improved. The division has continued to expand.

>< ><

The UK medical student pediatric group is now the Doane Fischer Society. After it was named for him in 2006, he attended monthly meetings and actively recruited students to become pediatricians until his death.

Dr. Wheeler had a banner year in 1972. He was elected president of the American Pediatric Society, an honor second only to the Howland Award for academic pediatricians. Those of us who went to the academic/research meetings that year attended the 10 a.m. plenary session to hear his speech: "Recollections of 40 Years of Hospitalization of

Children." (Presidential Address to the American Pediatric Society, May 24, 1972). We were all very proud of him, and his presidency called attention to our program.

When Dr. Wheeler retired in 1974 at the age of 65, which was the requirement at the time, he was very upset that some provision couldn't have been made for his continuation of service. Only a year later, he had an unexpected heart attack and died at home. Sad and shocked, I called my former mentor, Dr. Waldo E. Nelson, the long-time editor of the *Journal of Pediatrics*, asking him in a tearful voice to do a festschrift for Dr. Wheeler. He thought for a minute or two and then declined, saying that, and I remember his statement so well, "No, Charlton, Warren Wheeler doesn't meet the criteria for a festschrift. We all know that he was an excellent and wonderful bedside scientist, but he did not move pediatrics forward according to our guidelines for a festschrift." So ended the Wheeler era.

Reflecting on Dr. Wheeler's tenure, Dr. Noonan said "he was exactly who we needed at the time." The focus on hospital care from a chairman who was a "super chief resident" got a lot of things focused and did set the future path toward a children's hospital. In some ways, Dr. Wheeler was the prototype of "hospitalist" roles that are now in vogue and are transforming care. "Care-By-Parent" and many other things were ahead of their time. He moved pediatrics forward for Kentucky. Maybe Dr. Nelson was wrong.

CHAPTER 6

Breaking the Barrier

O n Monday, July 1, 1974, Jackie Noonan whirled out of her new office, hustled down the MN hall in her as-ever white coat toward morning report. I don't remember her ever being in the hospital without the white coat. One had to walk fast to keep up, and when she wasn't going directly somewhere, she was still in motion. Her residents dubbed it Brownian motion. After she took Dr. Wheeler's seat by the window, three over-the-weekend cases were presented and discussed, with most of the faculty present.

It was 20 years after the civil rights movement began, 10 years after President Johnson began his War on Poverty, and, less noticeable in Kentucky, 10 years into the women's liberation movement. There had never been a woman chair of a department in the century-old University except for the Department of Home Economics. When Dean Clawson attempted to call Noonan "Chairwoman," she insisted on being called "Chairman."

During the decade just past, the changes in the department largely had been forced by political changes outside the walls of the hospital. In Kentucky, particularly in Eastern Kentucky, many more people had access to never-before-available health care. The completion of the Mountain Parkway and Interstates 64 and 75 was bringing more and more patients, and our outreach clinics were expanding.

Now with Dr. Noonan and a well-seasoned clinical faculty, pressure came from within the walls of the hospital to change and improve patient care. I remember her statement that clinical dollars spend just as well as research dollars. We were well on our way to abandoning our original goal to be a demonstration University Hospital in favor of becoming a regional service University Hospital.

The most apparent need for us was to update our nurseries. The newborn nursery has always been the general pediatricians' exclusive turf, and we had fallen behind in its development.

**Jacqueline A. Noonan, M.D.,
Vermont, 1954
Chairman, 1974-1992
Dr. Noonan, just having
caught a toddler darting
around the clinic.**

Dr. Githens had foreseen the rapid development of neonatology and appointed Dr. John Boehm of the original eight faculty to be head of the nursery service. Jack Boehm would not be considered a neonatologist by modern standards, for there was no official way to become a neonatologist. Rather, Jack had been trained to perform manual microchemistries in Donough O'Brien's Pediatric Microchemistry Laboratory at the University of Colorado, although his clinical interest was in their sick baby nursery. But others also saw this need, so the nursery service at the hospital in Evanston, Ill., part of the Northwestern University Medical School, recruited Jack away from us to be their first neonatologist.

Several years later, Dr. Wheeler responded by hiring Dr. Robert Beargie from the University of Oklahoma, a student he had known at Ohio State. Bob moved his family to Lexington to assume his responsibility for the nursery, where sick infants as well as prematurely born babies were bedded. The standard "isolette" was the bed most used. It delivered regulated heat and oxygen, a great improvement over the open bassinet still used in most nurseries.

With an ever-expanding prematurely born and sick-baby patient population, the small space allotted was greatly overcrowded. Dr. Beargie had as many as twenty isolettes running at one time, with electric cords, vacuum lines, and oxygen lines all over the floor—a dangerous situation. The total space was what next became the ward pharmacy, and now is a remodeled waiting room.

Dr. Beargie's needs were great, but he was getting little or no administrative support. Dr. Wheeler was of little or no help. On his own, Dr. Beargie went to see the hospital administrator, Judge Culton, who was unsympathetic and just did not see the need for expanding or investing in neonatology, reminding Bob that we were a demonstration hospital, not a regional referral hospital. Nonetheless, we were receiving prematurely born babies from the small hospitals in Eastern Kentucky, typically wrapped in aluminum foil to retain body heat.

Dr. Beargie again went to Hospital Administration for help, and, eventually, Associate Hospital Director/Administrator Richard Corley actually walked up to the nursery with him. However, although Corley acknowledged that this special nursery situation was untenable, nothing happened or changed.

Consequently, soon afterward, Bob transferred to the Division of General Pediatrics and eventually to the Student Health Service, from where he retired. Ironically, when neonatology became a recognized pediatric subspecialty with board exams, Dr. Robert Beargie was "grandfathered" in. During the remainder of 1975-76, the nursery was attended by Dr. Linda Walters, a general pediatrician with some pediatric cardiology training, and by Dr. Nirmala Desai, who had had one year of neonatology training at Boston Hospital for Women, Boston, Mass. She had accompanied her husband to Lexington, where he established a private practice of urology. "Nima" was to provide the continuity needed in our NICU for the next 37 years.

Melvin Douglas Cunningham, M.D.
Director, Division of Neonatology
June 1, 1974-June 30, 1988

When Dr. Wheeler retired, he passed on the name of Dr. Douglas Cunningham to Dr. Noonan. Doug was finishing his neonatology fellowship under Louis Gluck, one of the original neonatologists, in San Diego, Calif. Doug's wife had family in Campbellsville, Ky., and the possibility of coming back to this area appealed to her. In the fall of 1973, Doug had simply phoned the Chairman of Pediatrics' office and spoken to Dr. Wheeler, asking him if a neonatology job was available in Kentucky. Later, Dr. Wheeler passed this information on to Dr. Noonan. Soon after, she contacted Dr. Cunningham and invited him to visit. What he found and what has happened can best be told in his own words, important because it chronicles the initial transition of the University of Kentucky Medical Center from a demonstration hospital to our present regional referral center with the mantra of providing "advanced care." Neonatology led the way. Doug's oral account is long but provides much of the flavor of the department's struggles to "keep up with the times." Paradoxically, everything seemed to move both too fast and too slow. Administrators resisted change; money was almost always the reason—and the answer.

Notes from an interview with Dr. Doug Cunningham, 05-21-09

In January of 1974 I came here for a visit and saw what had happened; when (Dr. Wheeler) retired, she (Dr. Noonan) had come on and had set her priorities as to what she wanted to do with the (neonatology) department. Of course, she had been here a number of years as a cardiologist, and I don't know what else was on the list, but near the top of the list was to reorganize the premature nursery into a neonatal intensive care unit, so she started the tour by showing me the normal newborn nursery downstairs, which looked like all the other newborn nurseries, rows of bassinetes with healthy screaming babies. Then she took me upstairs to show me where they were taking care of the premature babies. I think the pharmacy is that floor space presently; it's been many things, but back then it was the premature nursery and as we were walking down the hall, as you go down the hall on the fourth floor towards where the

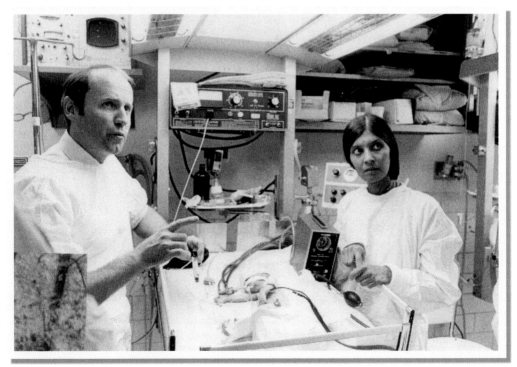

Dr. Cunningham and side-kick, Dr. Nirmala Desai, working with a prematurely born baby in a newly available raidant heat incubator.

patients were, just as we were approaching the elevator, the elevator doors opened in that bay and an x-ray machine rolled out ahead of us. So we were following it down the hallway, this fellow pushing a portable x-ray machine. It stopped and she said, "Here's the door, but we'll have to wait a second until they take the x-ray." And I thought "Oh, take x-ray of a baby." So we were standing, there in the hallway, and I could see that that was where we were going, but the x-ray was being taken right there in the hallway. I thought, "Premature baby getting an x-ray in the hallway, how could that be," but because this door was so small they couldn't go in with the x-ray machine. The next thing I know a window slides open and a nurse takes the baby out through the window, holds it, the x-ray guy goes click, the baby was handed back in with tubes and wires and things attached, and the window was shut. The x-ray guy backs up with the machine, and we step into the little adjacent room to wash our hands. I was stunned. They took that baby's x-ray. Jackie didn't understand why I was so astounded; she thought I was a little goofy, I guess. We washed up and walked in. They had a room to the left with two of the warming beds and two incubators, but four babies in this one room in very close quarters and all four of these babies were on respirators and obviously very tiny. Then there was a service area and two additional rooms that had incubators in them with premature babies being cared for. All told, in that small area they were able to take care of 15 or 16 sick babies. At an absolute pinch, they could go to 20, but it was very, very crowded. When babies were large enough, they would go out to the pediatric floor, and there was a room on the pediatric floor that was enclosed, and they would have 3 or 4 babies in that area who were in the final stages of being prepared to go home. The department also had a unique other wing that I had never heard of prior to that, neither in California, and it was called Care-By-Parent, which was perfect for a lot of reasons, for infants who had been in neonatal intensive care and were being prepared to go home. I don't know when they established it, but it was under Dr. Wheeler and had been here a long time as part of the program. When I saw it, it was such a uniquely perfect idea for patients getting ready to go home, because taking home a baby who wasn't a normal newborn by any means, had been in the hospital 3-4 weeks maybe, now weighing enough to go home, generally over 5 pounds in those days, but nowhere near a 7 or 8 pounder. Often they had a very young mother, so the baby would go in a bassinet to a room on what we called 4 North then, Care-By-Parent Unit. There would be a bed and chairs and things to accommodate a mother and father for a couple of nights, sometimes three nights. But they would stay there by the day, and nurses would come into the room frequently and teach the mother how to give medications if the baby needed special care, special handling of dressings or tubes or feeding or something of that nature. The mothers learned under the supervision of the nurses, but in an environment that if it didn't go right, within seconds other doctors or nurses would be available to help and stabilize the situation if it didn't work out. But it was a great transition for going home. I immediately saw its utility for that patient population. And so Jackie asked me if I was interested, and I said yes and she asked me what I did and I went through everything. She told me that the grant that was going to support these babies was money coming from the Johnson Administration's "Great Society." It was part of the overall civil rights legislation that he put through. But in addition to that, there was health advocacy monies in there and the intent was, not only to build on the changes of the demography in this country involving civil rights, but also to advance health care, so it was part of the wave that led to Medicare/Medicaid funding.

Q: Was the program part of the War on Poverty?

A: *Appalachia, of course, was very much a part of the War on Poverty, so she was saying how they had a whole network of clinics. Especially, Dr. Noonan had heart clinics (and to this day they continue to function), and she would see these sick babies out there, but getting them from there to here for this type of special care was going to be a real problem. I told her about flying babies in from the desert and using federal resources for helicopters, and I remember her just looking at me and thinking, that's a neat idea, but boy it's going to take something to make it happen, and it certainly isn't one of the first things we need to do. So she called me back after that visit and wanted to know if I was still interested, and I said, "Yeah, certainly," and she asked how much pulmonology have I had in training. I thought immediately of pulmonary physiology, basic research in physiology, and I tried to tell her what I did. She was a little impatient, she says "Well, we really need somebody who knows something about respirators." Oh, well wait a minute, if that's "pulmonology" to you. I started telling her about what I was doing out there with a room full of respirators and so forth and then she said okay, she'd call me back. So, one thing led to another, and I arrived here in July 1974. They were still taking x-rays out the window. Couldn't get the x-ray machine inside the door. I found when I got here that they had 20 incubators max, of which 12 were in good working order, and the other 6 or 7 could possibly be used, but there weren't parts for them. When I got down to the 3 or 4 oldest ones, they were so old the equipment man told me they just don't make parts for them anymore and we've got a couple more in the back, but we use them for parts. They were scavenging parts to keep these oldest ones running and so forth. So, I started my priorities with "We need more incubators." We needed new incubators, and new designs were rapidly coming out. The technology from 1975 to 1985 in miniaturization and electronics so that we could do monitoring on these tiny babies was being extracted from the adult experience, which was rapidly escalating as well, but this step to miniaturize things was difficult, and it took a while to do that, but we drew on that a great deal.*

Q: And there were new products on the market?

A: *Yes, there were new products out there, so it was funding; the money was the problem. The major priority was to get respirators. The new respirators were coming out, but in this country oxygen in a tank really wasn't a practical thing, apparently, until the second world war when they put oxygen in tanks into airplanes so they could fly at increased altitudes for long periods of time. At the end of the war, well, we've got oxygen in tanks, we've got people in hospitals with respiratory problems, we can give them a little oxygen, so they started doing that. Then they started doing it with preemies, 1948, 49, 50—gosh, they pinked up in a hurry, especially those tiny ones with lung disease. But by 1952 or 1953 we realized these babies were going blind, they were blinded by the oxygen, that's what they thought, and to this day it's still an issue. So boom, all the oxygen was taken out of the nurseries. In Europe, though, as they were rebuilding their medical systems in Western Europe, they were building respirators by the mid-50's for infants, little tiny respirators for infants and using oxygen. By 1960 we realized by not using oxygen and by having respirators we were saving prematures, but they had serious neurologic problems that maybe if we had been more aggressive in treatment for them, they would have survived more intact. And we're talking about prematures 3 ½ pounds and above in those days. Smaller ones were considered unsalvageable. So, in the 60's we began to use oxygen again and gradually it advanced so that by the late 60's we were using adult respirators that had been rigged with clamps to make them work for babies. By 1970 we were manufacturing infant ventilators. So the timing of those infant ventilators and the timing of Dr. Noonan saying, "We are going to move more aggressively with neonatal intensive care," and she also had in mind at this time that they wanted to move in the direction of surgery, being able to do more cardiac surgery, expand the pediatric surgery, and, to do that, she needed the intensive care unit to support those patients. That gave us a big push. So there was multiplicity, I think, in her overall plan for the department, and those things had not moved in that direction under the previous Chairman. But times had changed very quickly too, so she was keeping up with the times. We got some respirators in, but the more respirators we brought in, the sicker the babies were that came in, and we still couldn't get the x-ray machine in. We can't manage patients on respirators without x-rays. So I went down and met Judge Calton, the hospital administrator, and, of course, this was the 70's, early 70's, and the man had on a leisure suit with lapels that came out to his shoulders, wide tie, hair down below his ears, and he was smoking a pipe. It was just interesting. I began my spiels and my 5 minutes with the Administrator of the Hospital, and he said, "What do you need up there?" In an instant I changed my priorities, and I said, "I need more nurses. I've got all these babies that keep coming out of Eastern Kentucky as well as here, and I don't have enough trained nurses," and he said, "How many nurses do you need?" I said twelve to start with. "What else do you need?" He just went right on. And I said I need more incubators and I gave him a list of incubators, and I need more respirators. I hadn't really thought about the nursing part, about how difficult it was going to be and how much equipment we have and we need to have nurses who know how to use it and to take care of the babies. So the push and the shove began, and it was interesting. But eventually we got the nurses and eventually the incubators, eventually we got the respirators, and then we needed more space, and we needed to be able to get that x-ray machine inside there. So the next time I went down to see him I told him, "I need remodeling. We've got to make the doors bigger, we've got to stop taking x-rays of babies passed out the window into the hallway." At that point I began to see the heels dug into the dirt and I was told there was a man named Bosomworth, this all would have to go to him. So that was Dr. Peter Bosomworth, the Vice Chancellor for everything. A very difficult struggle began after that, and I don't know whether this book has room in it for the negatives, but when Chart asked me to think of all the things we*

JACKPOT! Dr. Doug Cunningham is reuinted with the first quadruplets born at UK (1986). The Quads were born after 32 weeks gestation and were patients in the NICU for six weeks. In this reunion photo they are age 3 months.

did, the problem I have had since talking with him was trying to put the positives in front of the negatives.

So, what happened was that it took two years to get my hands on what we needed and the people who were going to make a difference, but all along Dr. Noonan was right there, never saying no. But she didn't say anything when there was a need or an issue, she never stood in my way, she never said no and she always heard me out. And that I think was one of the things that kept me going, to change the care of newborn infants in Eastern Kentucky.

The second thing was, who was the first neonatologist? Well, there were no Board Certified neonatologists until 1975, and I was the first Board Certified neonatologist.

There were some very nasty administrative times where heads absolutely bumped. Dr. Bosomworth said, "The mission of this medical center is not tertiary care, it is primary care and the Area Health Regional Act and whatever else is going on, we've got to serve the people." I couldn't argue against that, it made perfect sense. But I said, "It's a medical center, it's a medical school, and Cincinnati is building a new neonatal intensive care unit, Louisville is building a neonatal intensive care unit, very active, one of the earliest in parallel with Cincinnati, a true neonatal intensive care unit, which started out as just premature nurseries under Dr. Billy

Andrews in Louisville as well as the group in Cincinnati." In the 1960's they saw this coming. I think it was right after I left medical school it really started to blossom in the late 1960's, as I saw it in California. It was happening there, and it wasn't happening here at the same level, but the time had come just by numbers of population, plus federal funding and the recognition of the War on Poverty and the needs of Appalachia. Plus the roads opened up. The first preemie that got transported here, we didn't transport him. This was a baby that came through the Emergency Room wrapped in aluminum foil with the mother. He was about 3 or 4 days old, and the mother had come from a small community somewhere way up, maybe in Hindman or Harlan, one of those areas, and had ridden in a coal truck down to another town, then had come by ambulance from there to the Emergency Room here. He had a nice blanket around him, a little tiny face, weighed about 3 ½ pounds. He was one of those prematures that are physically more mature, they're premature by weight, but physiologically he was more mature and so he didn't have respiratory distress, and he had been kept warm and had been fed enough so that the three days didn't make that much difference. But they weren't going to keep him any longer knowing that he really needed an incubator, and she told about riding all those miles in a coal truck down to someplace like London or Corbin and then they brought her on up the freeway. But the Mountain Parkways were opening and access now by vehicle was becoming available. Of course, I was thinking we could get in and out of there with a helicopter. So, everything in medicine was saying we need to do this, but expanding the program was contrary to the administration, beginning with Judge Calton and Dr. Bosomworth in the 1974-75-76 era. Well, once the pediatricians and family practitioners in Eastern Kentucky heard that I was here, Dr. Desai and Dr. Noonan were here, this was bound to happen. Also, it was the availability of pediatric surgeons, because taking premature babies from Eastern Kentucky all the way to Louisville was impractical, and they did it, but at great expense and sometimes without good results because it was too far. It was very difficult for Louisville to support them at those distances with their staff and needs and that area was growing rapidly, and they were getting patients from Southern Indiana because Indianapolis was at the same stage in evolving neonatal intensive care that Louisville and Cincinnati were. And when you get down in the southeastern corner of Kentucky, try to get to Cincinnati from there. There wasn't really any neonatal intensive care in Eastern Tennessee at that point. Knoxville had not developed a neonatal intensive care unit at that time; it came soon thereafter. So the demand was there and then we were at capacity, 25 babies. We were taking beds away from General Pediatrics to put our babies in. And then a condition called necrotizing enterocolitis entered into the picture, which is still a problem today. But in those years it tended to come in waves, where these babies would develop a severe intestinal infection, some requiring surgery, and it appeared in clusters so that we thought it was communicable. I think this disease was historically important to us because we needed to isolate these babies, we didn't want the other babies to get it. So where do we isolate them? We had to take portions of the space that we had and block it off, or we had to take them out of there and put them on general pediatrics, but the nurses on general pediatrics hadn't had neonatology training to take care of these babies, which also took nurses out of the unit. So it created some terrible problems for us. One of the problems that has been known for 100 plus years, if you have an infectious disease problem, you have to isolate patients, No. 1. No. 2 you have to minimize the crowding. So what I did was, if we were at our maximum, 25 patients, and we had necrotizing enterocolitis in one section of the area, when we got a call, I had to turn down the patients. And when you say no, I'm not going to take care of a patient as a physician, Hippocrates rolls over in his grave, and everybody since him is going to say there's something wrong. What we said was, we can't take care of any more babies here because if we keep bringing in babies, they're going to die here. No. 1, we don't have the equipment; No. 2, we don't have the nurses; No. 3, I don't have the space; and No. 4, we're faced with this problem that babies are dying from this anyway, or they'll need surgery and then need even more care after surgery. So, you've got to take the baby to Cincinnati or Louisville or to Morgantown, W. Va., or Huntington could take care of a couple, and the doctors would do it. But they would howl because there were now younger pediatricians in their practices in Somerset, and Somerset, in particular, really would raise a stink when this happened. And it was because they were very good pediatricians and they had both older pediatricians and younger pediatricians there, and they knew that what the difference could be if they had neonatal intensive care. Then when Cincinnati was full and Louisville was full, they were saying no, or, if they weren't saying no, they were really upset about having to go over census on their own, and they didn't like going all the way to, well, Maysville was about as far as they wanted to go. They sure didn't want to go to London or Somerset to pick up a baby, and those communities didn't have the ability to move them that far. So, it's now about 1978, and, here in town, St. Joseph had closed their OB and nursery down, shut it down. Sister over there said, "You know, we're just not going to do obstetrics and nursery care anymore." So, Baptist was of course the next busy place, along with Good Sam. When they had sick babies, they didn't have neonatal intensive care, so they expected to send their babies across town, and we were full-up. Well, it got even more difficult and they said, "Why are you doing this, why can't you take these babies?" I had 21 beds, I think I was licensed for 21, but we would go to 25, but then we were up against a wall, we just couldn't. Interesting thing, Dr. Noonan understood that and she would stand behind me. I don't know what she had to endure at the administrative levels with Mr. Judge Calton and Dr. Bosomworth, but she knew it was right, so she stood with me. You can't keep cramming babies into a room with the expectation that they're going to get intensive care. So, the first thing that happened somewhere in the 1976 period was that they did make that door bigger and remodeled that area so that we had enough oxygen outlets.

Q: Did you get an expanded space then?

A: *We didn't get more space, we got space that we could work in better, but we didn't get beds particularly. So, I think he was at Lexington Clinic, but there was a pediatrician in town named Robert Beshear, and I met him through another friend in town named Linda Harvey, and I'm sure if you go to the files at the Herald-Leader you'll find her name.*

Q: Yes, she has worked a lot of with advocacy programs.

A: *Oh, all kinds of programs. She had twins herself, they were bigger twins, but they were still small, so she was very sensitive to the needs for parents with twins and preemies and so forth. The two of them teamed up to say, "What can we do to help you solve this problem of babies' being turned away?" I basically told them the same story I just told you. Here we are, I showed them around. Bob says, "Well, I think my brother can help us, let's see." His brother's name was Steve Beshear, who was a state representative and he came to visit.*

J. Robert Beshear, M.D., was a Duke Medical 1967 graduate and trainee, and he knew of our needs and what other university medical centers were doing. His plan was first to bring the need for a regional NICU to the awareness of the public, then request assistance from the legislature. As the state legislature convened in January 1976, Rep. Steve Beshear, now Governor Beshear, submitted House Bill 613 (1976) to

fund the remodeling and running of a Neonatal Intensive Care Unit in Lexington and the radio coverage area. Each time a neonatal transport was diverted to either Cincinnati or Vanderbilt, it would immediately be reported. There the radio jockey would put it out on the airwaves where live telephone calls would come into the station with all sorts of comment.

All the while, the Medical School and University Hospital were insisting that we did not need an NICU for our teaching, but the state needed it. The state legislature in early 1978 appropriated the money for us to have a state-of-the-art NICU, level-3. Along with this came the organization of all the nurseries in hospitals that delivered babies: a level-1 nursery allowed for the delivery of low-risk babies; a level-2 nursery allowed for the delivery of babies with some problems; and level-3 nurseries allowed for the delivery of babies that were at greatest risk. The University of Kentucky and the University of Louisville have the only nurseries designated level-3. This has reduced the number of birthing hospitals in Kentucky.

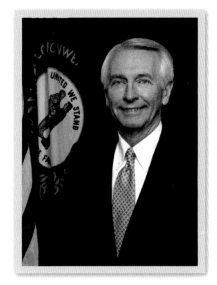

Gov. Steve Beshear. During three terms as state representative, Beshear helped modernize the Kentucky Judicial System and proposed legislation that resulted in the modernization and more than doubling of neonatal capacities at the University of Kentucky Hospital.

In an interview, Doug Cunningham also spoke of the amount of the legislative appropriation and how it changed the NICU:

> *The final support was $2.2 million as I recall; it was what came through on the bill, and construction started by taking the Care-by-Parent Unit, about half of it, and they put in temporary outlets and things, so that we could move the premature babies out of the premature area in there temporarily and care for them in that Care-by-Parent space while they began the construction of the new nursery. Anyway, it*

opened in 1981, a new Neonatal Intensive Care Unit that had space for 50 babies. We could get 50 in there if we had to. By this time, we'd inched up to almost 30 in the facilities that had been remodeled yet again; there were two remodels of the original space with some expansion, and then the big construction began, and it opened in 1981. But it was only licensed for 35. We filled that up right away. It was years later that I learned that it actually went to 50, and now Dr. Bricker is talking about 100 plus in the new hospital. But, in that period of time from 1974 to 1978 to 1982, the medical center changed. Dr. Bosomworth's approval of tertiary care became a reality; Judge Calton retired.

HB 613 - Beshear
Appropriate $1,500,000 for each fiscal year of the 1976-78 biennium to the Neonatal Intensive Care Unit at the Unversity of Kentucky Albert B. Chandler Medical Care Center, to increase the capacity of such unit from the existing 17 beds to 45 beds.

Feb 24 - to Appropriations and Revenue
Feb 25 - posted in committee
Mar 3 - reported favorably, 1st reading, to Calendar with committee amendment (1) redefining such appropriation as an amount not to exceed $3,000,000 for fiscal year 1977-78, from funds accruing as a result of surplus in official revenue estimates as of June 30, 1977
Mar 4 - 2nd reading, to Rules Mar 10 - recommitted to State Government

SR12 (BR1031) - Huff
Declare support for giving top priority in the 1978-80 Executive Budget to a 58-bed neo-natal unit at the University of Kentucky Medical Center.

Jan 23 - Appropriations and Revenue
Jan 31 - reported favorably, 1st reading, to Calendar
Feb 1 - 2nd reading, to Rules
Feb 9 - posted for passage, Feb 10
Feb 10 - adopted by voice vote

(From Legislative Record 1978)

A two pounder!

Historically, Kentucky has lagged behind in taking care of its children. In 1960, when our Department of Pediatrics began, the infant (birth to 1-year) death rate was 17:1000. The tiny and very tiny babies we now salvage weren't even counted. Now, almost fifty years later, the rate is 7.5:1000. This dramatic decline is due, in part, to our department's being here. Moreover, I attribute most of this advance to the improvement in nursery care, particularly the presence of our tertiary level Neonatal Intensive Care Unit. It is ironic that the first baby admitted to our new and expanded NICU arrived via coal truck, part way, from Harlan. Today, our department is a 30-minute helicopter ride from Harlan, with a transport team and equipment providing care throughout the flight. Outside of Lexington, only the larger hospitals deliver babies, and midwifery has all but disappeared.

After the tumultuous years Doug Cunningham spent bringing neonatology to Central and Eastern Kentucky, he moved back to San Diego, Calif., to re-enter the neonatal intensive care movement there. Eventually, his entrepreneurial spirit led him to invest in and to direct a national neonatal intensive care consortium, Pediatrix. One of their units is the NICU at Central Baptist Hospital in Lexington. He still has ties to the University of Kentucky, and he and his wife live here part of each year, and, when he is in town, teaches neonatology fellows.

Following Doug's departure, Dr. Noonan recruited one of his first neonatology Fellows to return and head up the Neonatology Division: Tom Pauly, M.D. He continued what Doug had started, with an almost-always-full 50-bed unit. Tom died from complications of pancreatic cancer in 2004. The chief of the division that followed Tom is Henrietta Bada-Ellzey, M.D. She runs our current 66-bed NICU and will be inheriting the 100-bed NICU unit scheduled to open as the construction is completed in 2016. Currently, there are seven neonatologists on faculty, along with six neonatology post-doctoral Fellows.

While there was much energy spent getting the UK Neonatology Division up and running, the rest of the department was also growing, teaching at multiple levels and delivering patient care, and literally bursting at the seams. The weekly schedule reflects this:

Monday	7:30-8:15 a.m.	Ward rounds
	8:15-9:15 a.m.	Morning report
	11 a.m.-noon	Attending rounds
	Noon-1 p.m.	Housestaff conference
	3-4 p.m.	Neonatal x-ray conference
	4:30-5:30 p.m.	Sign-out rounds

Present-day NICU doctors. (Dr. "Por" Sithisarn joined the faculty shortly after this photo was taken.)

Tuesday	7:30-8:15 a.m.	Ward rounds
	11 a.m.-noon	X-ray conference (ward)
	Noon-1 p.m.	Housestaff conference
	3-4 p.m.	Neonatal x-ray conference
	4:30-5:30 p.m.	Sign-out rounds
Wednesday	7:30-8:15 a.m.	Ward rounds
	11 a.m.-noon	Housestaff conference
	3-4 p.m.	Neonatal x-ray conference
	4:30-5:30 p.m.	Sign-out rounds
Thursday	7:30-8:15 a.m.	Ward rounds
	8:15-9:15 a.m.	Pediatric Grand Rounds
	11 a.m.-noon	X-ray conference
	Noon-1 p.m.	Housestaff conference (morbidity/mortality conference first Thursday)
	3-4 p.m.	Neonatal x-ray conference
	4:30-5:30 p.m.	Sign-out rounds
Friday	7:30-8:15 a.m.	Ward rounds
	8:15-9:15 a.m.	Morning report
	11 a.m.-noon	Attending rounds
	Noon-1 p.m.	Housestaff conference
	3-4 p.m.	Neonatal x-ray conference
	4:30-5:30 p.m.	Sign-out rounds

During Dr. Noonan's first six-year term as chairman, she hired additional clinical faculty, always seeking the hard-to-find subspecialists. However, our appearances on the national research stage were declining.

Our story so far has dwelt on staff and resources, but pediatricians in general have always shown a special extramural connection to the very young. Random acts of special caring occur regularly. One very special act of caring occurred with a small boy, Carl. His doctor was Carol Cottrill, M.D., a budding cardiologist at the time. Carol herself was from the mountains by way of Over-The-Rhine in Cincinnati, which makes the relationship even more special. The little boy was so sick she took him home with her. Carl's story as told by Dr. Cottrill follows:

Sitting there on his mother's lap was a two-year-old with a swollen belly who looked a little blue to me. I introduced myself to his mother, Mary, and asked what the little boy's name was. Carl wasn't terribly clean or well-dressed and neither was his mom, but I just wanted to discharge my responsibility about the abnormal EKG I had found and go home. I learned from Mary that Carl had been seen in one of the traveling General Pediatric Clinics (in Salyersville, Ky.—about 115 miles from Lexington) and the doctors examining him found an enlarged liver, so he was to be admitted (to the next available bed) to have a liver work-up.

Knowing that right heart enlargement and a large liver go together in congestive heart failure, I asked Mary if I could listen to him. He had a chest deformity (from his enlarged heart pushing against his immature ribs). He had a right ventricular heave and a very loud second heart sound, suggesting the presence of pulmonary artery hypertension. We didn't have

cutaneous oxygen monitors or echocardiography then, but I began developing a list of what might be his problem (doctors call it a differential diagnosis, usually constructed with the most likely item first). By a process of elimination, I diagnosed

Carl, on one of his better days, with Dr. Carol Cottrill and her newest rescued baby.

idiopathic pulmonary hypertension, a rare disorder that isn't usually seen in children. I agreed that he should be admitted, but arranged for him to be on the Cardiology Service, rather than the General Pediatric Service.

The next day, I took a proper history from Mary, learning that her first child, Sheridan, had been cared for by Dr. Noonan for some kind of heart issue and that Sheridan had died at age two. Mary got a far away look when she said "he just died in my arms." I later learned from Jackie that Sheridan had died of primary (or idiopathic) pulmonary hypertension. Her second child was also a boy, but she was afraid for his health too, so she gave him to her sister to raise for her. Her next child, Faye, was a young teen-ager. After that, she had a boy who died from pneumonia, followed by Tressie (named for her red hair), then Ronnie and Walt, then Carl. After Carl, Martha was born, and Theresa was an infant. They lived in an area of Salyersville called Rock House, which was "back a branch" meaning along a creek-bed. I told Mary that Carl had a serious disease and the way to tell about it was by cardiac catheterization. She gave permission and the next day he underwent that procedure. My fears were realized, as we found primary pulmonary hypertension and deduced that it was the familial type, since Sheridan also had it.

In trying to tell Mary in a gentle way, she refused eye contact, and said that she would walk all the way back home if she could. From that, I deduced that she didn't want to hear what I had to say. I asked Carl if he would like to have anything and he said he wanted a big red apple and a dime, which I provided. I came back later to check on him and tried to talk to Mary. She didn't act as if she understood what I was talking about until I finally said that Carl had the same disease that Sheridan had. She teared up with that and asked "when can we go home?"

I explained that Carl could go home the next day, with some medicines (diuretics and digoxin) in the hope of helping with his right heart failure for a while.

Over the next couple of years he was seen sporadically at a regional clinic nearby. Often he would be out of medicine. Since the general peds folks went to his area, they saw him occasionally, even making a "house call," finding all of the children barefoot in the snow in February. Mary remained taciturn, speaking little in response to our questions about Carl. I thought that she was doing the best she could.

Carl was supposed to come to the regional clinic in Prestonsburg, as one of the nurses thought he wasn't doing as well. When he got there, he was very cyanotic (blue) and swollen. I asked Mary how long he had been blue, to which she answered, "He's had a right smart cold for a couple of weeks." In response to a query about his swelling, she said, "I just noticed it now." I told her he was going to have to come to the hospital, and she said she couldn't come because of the other children.

I told her to give me a note, allowing me to take care of his medical needs, and his medical card, so that I could admit him to the hospital. We got some Lasix from the local hospital and gave him a dose. He weighed 42 pounds in the clinic. We finished the clinic and took a gallon milk bottle in the car with us; his Lasix (a diuretic) worked all the way to the hospital, where he weighed 36 pounds. The first thing he wanted to do was to take a bath, and he played in the tub until the nurses made him get out to go to bed.

Over the next few days, he acclimated to our medicines. With the holiday season approaching, I bought him a book about Christmas, and he learned to make jigsaw puzzles. At 4 years of age, he had not been to school yet. One morning when we were making rounds, he was looking at his book and laughing. Since it wasn't a funny book, I asked him what he was laughing at. He said, "Lookie here, them people cut down a tree and put it in their house. Whoever heard of a tree in a house?" and laughed about it again.

I dreaded sending him home, because I didn't think I'd ever see him again alive. His time at home, though, was short-lived as he was admitted again in late November with an exacerbation of heart failure. This time, we taught him to take his own medicine. To test his ability, I asked Mary if he could spend the Thanksgiving weekend with our family, taking his medicines without prompting.

He was excited about everything at our house. One of his early observations: "It never gets too hot in your house" led to a trip to the basement and an explanation about how the thermostat worked. He then said, "Reckon if I dug a basement under my mama's house she could get one of those?"

Thanksgiving Day brought a lot of company (in addition to our large family). Carl was quiet and particularly skeptical of the foods he'd never seen before. He looked suspiciously at the turkey and said, "I don't think I want any of that beast." I told him I would give him a very small piece which he could try, and if he didn't like it, he didn't have to eat the rest. The meal was half over when he tugged at my elbow and said, "I believe I'll have a little more of that pork."

After proving his ability to take his medicine, on the Sunday after Thanksgiving, Tom and I drove him back home. In addition to his medicines, he wanted to take his Sesame Street blue jump-suit which I had picked out for him. We packed up toys, clothes that we knew fit him, and set off for Salyersville. On the way, we stopped to get apples, bread, peanut butter, milk, and other rather staple foods for the family. I gave him some money to hide in his shoe, in case he had to get in touch with me, and told him, "If you ever swell up again, you must find me."

When we got to his house, we found a two-room house without furniture; all the kids and dogs were crouched around a stove in one room to keep warm. When we brought in the food, there was no place to put it except on the floor, and the children tore open the bags as if they hadn't had food for days. After a brief visit, we left just as darkness was falling and the fog was rising from the creek. Tom and I were each worried—he wondered how he was going to get us out of there safely, and I worried that I'd never see Carl again.

The next month was uneventful, with me working and Tom seeing to the children. We wondered about Carl, but didn't talk about him much. It was an avoided topic. I prayed a lot, though. Christmas came and went, and at the end of January, I got a call from the local health department, telling me that Carl was there.

He was picked up on the Mountain Parkway by a truck driver with his Sesame Street jump suit in a paper bag, trying to hitch-hike to Lexington (115 miles) to find me. I got Mary on the phone (she had arrived at the health department, too). Carl was swollen again, because he ran out of medicine and Mary hadn't filled his prescription. She had used his shoe money to buy cigarettes, so he had no way to call me. I arranged for Carl to be readmitted, and told Mary, "Mary, he's going to die, but he's going to die earlier because you won't take care of him," to which she replied, "Will you do that for me?"

I thought at first that I hadn't heard her correctly. I had so many mixed feelings that I had to go to my beloved Newman Center to pray. I talked to Father Moore, telling him that Mary had asked me to take care of Carl. He told me I would have to make a commitment to help Carl die. I said I really wanted to help him live a little first, but he reminded me again that I'd have to help him die. After this, I called a man I really respect, Dr. Otto Kaak, a child psychiatrist, to ask him what he thought it would do to my normal children to bring a dying child into our home. He wisely told me that my children's attitudes about death would be what mine are. If I didn't see death as a terrible thing, they wouldn't either.

When Carl was discharged, he came to our house as a foster child. This began a real adventure, with our family learning about Eastern Kentucky living and Carl learning about life in middle-class America.

We found that he liked to eat paper, because "then you don't get hungry." Taking all his paper away resulted in his tearing off bits of wallpaper to eat. He hoarded food, and I often found crackers (and crumbs) in his sock drawer, and apples under his stack of shirts. But he was faithful about taking his medicine.

After he took his diuretics, he would have to go to the bathroom, and was always interrupting something to use the bathroom. He loved to wash his hands with good smelling stuff. One time, Benjamin asked, "What's up with this kid—he's always in the bathroom." I told Benjamin about the medicine's making him go to the bathroom, but also said, "One of the reasons Carl likes the bathroom is that he didn't have one at his house."

I told Benjamin that Carl had to go out to a tiny little outhouse to go to the bathroom.

Carl corrected me: "NO, I didn't; we didn't have one."

I said, "You didn't have a bathroom outside the house?"

"No."

"Carl, where did you go to the bathroom?"

Shrugging his shoulders, he said, "Offen the porch."

So we learned about Eastern Kentucky sanitation, and the bathroom wasn't discussed again.

Carl started school at St. Paul's with our other children. He loved school and really loved his first grade teacher, Mrs. Hutchinson. She was like a grandmother to him, her affection for him matched by Mrs. Stewart, who helped us at home. He had trouble walking up and down stairs, so at lunch time, the eighth grade boys carried him up and down the steps.

Carl remained with us, and we took him to visit his family every month. The drive to Salyersville was punctuated with questions. "Ms. Stewart says there ain't never no cause to hit a baby." I told him I agreed with that. "Then why does my mom hit Sammy (Mary's newest baby)?" Carl now had a total of nine siblings. More questions: "Why did Ronnie and Walt hit me in the stomach when they knew it would hurt with my big liver?" That was hard to answer, although I knew that boredom in Eastern Kentucky was in a large part why parents abuse their children and that their older children abuse the younger ones.

Carl was an obedient and very personable child who did not require very much in the way of discipline. I don't ever remember giving him time-out, or taking privileges away. He told us about his former diet. Every morning, the kids would walk to the mouth of the branch to a store called "May's." There they would each get a pop and either chips or a honey bun and walk back home with their meal for the day. I knew that the children were all put into foster care for a period while Mary was supposed to be learning housekeeping skills in another home. After a month, she still couldn't fry an egg. She answered, "Ain't no sense to learn to fry an egg; ain't got no stove to fry one on."

But Carl became interested in cooking and his favorite place was perched on the edge of the counter, reading the recipes to me or to Ms. Stewart. One day as we were cooking, he asked me out of the blue, "Do you think I'm going to die before Benjamin?" I thought a minute and then said that it was true that he was sicker than Benjamin and had to take more medicines than Benjamin did, but that God, in his wisdom, doesn't let us know when we are going to die. I told him that if you had one row of 100 sick people and another row of 100 well people, that probably one of the sick persons would die before the well ones would start to die. I ended the discussion by saying, "You know, Benjamin could run in the street tomorrow and be killed by a car—like I said, God doesn't let us know when we are to die, because we couldn't enjoy our life if we were waiting for death." Carl seemed satisfied, and said, "If'n I die first, I'll be up there a'waitin' for you; me and Chrissie (he knew I had a daughter who died many years before)."

One of the things Carl really wanted to do was to go to Disney World. He also wanted to see an island. We all went to Disney World in the summer and had a really good time.

Carl made the decision to be baptized into the Catholic faith, and he and Father Moore became friends, talking about all sorts of things. He made his First Communion in the same class with our daughter, Hope, and we had a good brunch at the Hyatt to celebrate.

Carl's mother decided to move to Xenia, Ohio, and we offered to adopt Carl at that time. She was willing, so we did a private, direct adoption from her to Tom and me. She went to live with a man there. Once they came to visit Carl, so Carl was meeting this man for the first time. Mary said to Carl, "Come over here and sit on your new dad's lap." Carl obviously was shrinking from this person, so I said, "Why not let Carl sit on your lap, Mary; I'm sure he's missed you." Carl shot me a grateful glance and sat on his mother's rather pregnant lap. After the visit was over, Carl came to me and said, "My momma didn't smell so good." I reminded him of the lack of sanitary facilities where he lived before, which softened his attitude toward Mary.

We decided to take another child into foster care—a terminally ill little girl, Virginia. While Virginia was dying in the hospital, Tom took the children, Benjamin, Hope, and Carl, out to fly kites, to talk about things that you could feel but not see (the wind, emotions). Tom asked each of them what would happen if their kite got loose. Carl said if his kite got loose, it would fly over the countryside so he could see the house he used to live in with his mother, he would see the school he went to and all of his friends.

As time went by, Carl's condition changed. He had less congestive heart failure but changed to a low cardiac output state. He had less energy, but continued to attend school. Some days, he would take his pillow and lie on the floor for some of the day. We treated every day as a gift, which it was. Usually, in the face of congestive failure, the life of a person with pulmonary hypertension is fairly short, particularly in children with primary pulmonary hypertension. We were blessed to have more than five years with him.

As Carl got sicker, I knew that if he was to see an island it would have to be soon. I was looking around for an island in the Ohio River, but Tom felt that if it was Carl's wish to see an island, we should go to an island in style. So we took the kids out of school for two weeks and Carl, Virginia, Benjamin, and Hope spent that wintry January in St. Croix, basking in the sun, going to the beach, picking out our own lobsters from the fish market, and joining the islanders at an Epiphany party. Carl came back rejuvenated for a while.

When he could no longer go to school, we got a home-bound teacher for him; he impressed her (as he did everyone) with his willingness to accept ideas, his sense of humor, and his openness. A good example of his openness happened one day when he really felt bad. Mornings were particularly hard for him. He felt so bad that he called Father Moore and said, "You know, Father Moore, that I'm dying. I think you'd better come and give me Communion and pray with me." Father Moore came over, and when he rang the doorbell, Carl (who by now was up and Ms. Stewart had given him something to eat and drink so that he felt better) answered the bell and said to Father Moore, "I made a mistake—it's not going to be today."

Christmas came, with our usual trim-the-tree party. The children's program on Christmas Eve, Midnight Mass. Then Carl's eleventh birthday was Jan. 31. The Todd kids brought him birthday presents, but his cardiac output was so low he really didn't know what he was seeing. I covered the situation by saying, "Oh, look, Carl, at all the pretty colored markers, and there's this special one that is white that erases the others." I really don't think the children knew he was feeling so bad.

In February, Tom was going out to the farm we owned in Mercer County to meet the exterminators, who were to spray for termites. Carl went along, and because Tom didn't want him exposed to the chemicals, Carl went to our neighbor, Beth Glaser's house. Beth and Carl took the big truck out to move some horses and he had a good time sitting up on a cushion to see everything. They then came home, and Carl complained that his back hurt. Beth told him to lie down on the couch and called Tom. By the time Tom arrived, Carl had very quietly died.

We had made a plan that if Carl got very sick or died, Tom would page me, and we would meet in the Emergency Department at University Hospital. Tom brought Carl there and, when he arrived, Carl had died. I was holding Carl's body in the emergency room, when one of the priests I knew, Father Larry Hehman, came in. He was in the ER with an elderly parishioner who had fractured her wrist. As we were talking, Dr. Noonan came in with the autopsy papers. Father Hehman said, "You're not going to have an autopsy, are you? After all, you know why he died." I couldn't help but try to educate Larry a little, telling him that frequently other things are found at autopsy that were unsuspected during life. And besides, I said, "Where do you think the material comes from that medical students use to study? Where do their slides of normal skeletal muscle come from? It's really a way for part of us to live forever in the knowledge that we give to our students."

Carl's funeral was well attended by the kids with whom he had gone to school at St. Paul's. They had learned songs and picked special *readings, and his friend, Father Moore, made everyone understand that death is only the beginning of another kind of life that will probably be a lot more fun than the one we have here.*

Mary's daughter, Faye, married at fifteen years of age and had three children within four years. The year after Carl died, Faye, her husband, and all three of the children were killed in an accident when the car they were riding in crossed the center line to hit a coal truck head-on. The social workers in Xenia contacted me about Mary's family. It seems that Ronnie and Walt (the boys immediately older than Carl) had become the town bad boys and were about to go to juvenile detention. The social worker said when she talked to Mary, all Mary would do is rock back and forth in a catatonic state and complain about the high cost of food these days.

Mary's life consisted of tragedy. She was about my age, from roughly the same socio-economic background, but by the time she was 45 years old, she had lost four children and three grandchildren. She held Sheridan as he died. Her guilt over his death led her to give another son away. Her fear of Carl's impending death made it impossible for her to care for him properly. And Faye's and the babies' deaths were more than she could tolerate. No wonder the "catatonic state." It was probably safer than the real world for her.

As for Carl's legacy, our family continued to foster and adopt children. We learned a lot from Carl about life, death, and love. He gave us the courage to share our home with thirty other children over the years from as close as Lexington and as far away as Nigeria, Guatemala, and Ecuador. As Father Hehman said, "… born … died … and lived happily after."

Sadly, Carl's story highlights the multiple burdens of poverty, ignorance, and illness of many children at that time. Besides his heart trouble, the central cause of Carl's misery was poverty. Poor health and economic poverty go hand-in-hand, with Kentucky near the bottom in both (thank God for Mississippi!). The major reason is that half their parents have no secure employment in the form of a year-round, full-time job. Education is lacking. In 1960, you were unlikely to find a graduate from the previous year's high school class still living in either a mountain county or in many rural counties. Education reform ushered in by former Gov. Bert Combs by legal action after he left office has greatly improved this situation—but we still have far to go.

Everyone knew Carl and his story; we watched Dr. Cottrill with great respect for having taken this child into her home. Over the years, Dr. Cottrill and her husband, Tom Rolfes, a former Catholic priest, have taken 30 more homeless sick children into their home for lengthy periods.

CHAPTER 7

Evolution of the Subspecialties

As Dr. Noonan continued her chairmanship, she was faced with new expectations brought about by advances in pediatrics and medicine in general. Historically, infections comprised the major causes of childhood morbidity and mortality in the United States, and a general pediatrician was the infectious disease expert in the private practice world. As vaccines and antibiotics were developed, and infectious diseases in children began to be brought under control, we began to appreciate disorders of the underlying organ systems. After World War II, post-residency subspecialty training programs began to appear that focused on these underlying problems.

Originally, a pediatrician could take additional study in a particular organ system and its disorders and become a subspecialist. The establishment of a subspecialty typically was driven by the introductions of new technologies, equipment, or techniques that allowed us to rescue more children. For Dr. Noonan's own subspecialty, pediatric cardiology, she states that when Robert Gross ligated a patent ductus in 1938, her discipline was born. Additional diagnostic and imaging techniques allowed surgical and other treatments of congenital heart defects. Pediatric cardiology became the first subspecialty certification board in 1961.

To maintain quality of care, the American Board of Pediatrics added training requirements and examinations to be certified in a pediatric subspecialty. The growth of general pediatrics and subspecialty pediatrics is shown on the following page in Table 7-1.

Almost all pediatric subspecialists practicing in UK's Department of Pediatrics are "board certified." During Dr. Noonan's chairmanship, it became her job to attract and hire pediatric subspecialists to come to Kentucky, typically with not a lot to offer them. In this chapter are the stories of the most critical subspecialty divisions, the necessary resource to bring advanced care to Kentucky's children.

Table 7-1: Subspecialty Pediatric Boards and Diplomates (2008)

Certifying Board	Year Founded	Certifying Board	Year Founded
General Pediatrics (ABP)	1932	Neurodevelopmental Disabilities	2001
		Developmental-Behavioral	2002
ABP-Certified Pediatric Subspecialties		Transplant Hepatology	2006
Cardiology	1961	Sleep Medicine	2007
Hematology-Oncology	1974	Hospice/Palliative Medicine	2008
Nephrology	1974		
Neonatology-Perinatology	1975	**Other Certified Subspecialties**	
Endocrinology	1978	Pediatric Neurology	1969
Pulmonology	1986	Allergy-Immunology	1973
Critical Care	1987	Pediatric Surgery	1975
Gastroenterology	1990	Medical Genetics	1981
Emergency Medicine	1992	**Subparts:**	
Rheumatology	1992	General Clinical Genetics	
Sports Medicine	1993	Cytogenetics	
Adolescent Medicine	1994	Dysmorphology	
Infectious Diseases	1994	Biochemical Genetics	
Medical Toxology	1994	Molecular Genetics	

Data from the American Boards of Pediatrics, Allergy and Immunology, Neurology, Medical Genetics, and Surgery, 2009

NEUROLOGY

Our College of Medicine was the beneficiary of a continental-shelf shift in neurology in the early 1960s. Until then, physicians with expertise in neurologic disorders were housed in a division of the Departments of Medicine or Pediatrics and used primarily as consultants. Our department began with Fred Horner, M.D., a pediatric neurologist from the University of Colorado, Denver. But when Chairman Jack Githens left UK in June 1963, Fred left too. I remember that on the evening he left, we had to pull him away from reading adult EEGs so he could make his flight to Rochester, N.Y., his next academic stop.

The whole hospital then had to depend on Les Blakey, M.D., from the Lexington Clinic. He was the only neurologist left in town. The neurology search committee could not find an academic neurologist willing to come to Kentucky as a division head in either Medicine or Pediatrics. Then they learned that David Clark, the pediatric neurologist at Johns Hopkins, was unhappy and began to woo him. At Hopkins, Dr. Clark could not admit a patient and be the attending physician, only a consultant. On many of those cases, he felt he could care for the patient better than the patient's designated pediatric attending. Finally, he agreed to come to Kentucky if he could have his own department.

Dr. Willard agreed. Clark is well remembered at Hopkins, where his portrait hangs in the medical library.

Once Clark was in Kentucky (1965), we knew he was here. He was all over the pediatric wards and frequently made night rounds. When I was the attending pediatrician, I could always ask him for help on a tough case—he would carefully listen to the history and examine the baby himself—I was usually reassured that I was managing the case correctly.

At the administrative level, things were different. His first shot across our bow was to demand half of the third-year Children's Student Clerkship, six of the 12 weeks. I'm not sure how this was resolved, but he got a hunk of the 12-week rotation. Next, he wanted to be the attending physician for all the meningitis and encephalitis cases in children. This was Dr. Wheeler's turf, and a long standoff resulted. When Clark couldn't get the hospital auditorium for a daytime Grand Rounds, he turned the lemons he was handed into lemonade.

David B. Clark, Ph.D. 1939, University of Chicago; M.D. 1946, University of Chicago. (Dissertation: "The Human Spinal Cord Twenty Years After Total Transection")

Robert Baumann, M.D., relates that on Tuesday evenings, from 7-9 p.m., there was a weekly conference with an audience of 50 to 70, where the housestaff would present their most difficult neurologic patients. Clark would retake the history, do the examination, and announce his diagnosis. Then the laboratory or biopsy data were presented, and a final diagnosis made. He was almost always right. Clark published relatively few articles, but he was a constant visiting professor in the United States, Australia, and England; he wrote chapters in a number of neurology textbooks.

In 1967, Clark brought with him two faculty members, Doug Jameson, M.D. (Wisconsin) and Mike McQuillin, M.D. (Johns Hopkins). Soon followed his housestaff—Ian Hopkins (Australia), Bob Haslam (Canada), and Herb Swick (Alaska). Bob Haslam is the current chairman of pediatrics at the University of Toronto. Very early in Clark's Kentucky career, he gave faculty status to a medical social worker, Mary Leonadakes. In addition to keeping follow-ups organized, she kept his clinical papers and notes in order. Bill Markesberry and Robert Baumann were his next faculty appointments. Clark retired as chairman of Neurology in 1979, but continued as chief of Neurology at our Veterans' Hospital in Lexington until his death following cardiac surgery years later.

The Department of Neurology lists 26 M.D. faculty members with Drs. Bob

Baumann, Bill Robertson, Farjam Farzam, and Qutubuddin Kahn serving as pediatric neurologists. Clark, in his Osler style of teaching, left his mark on all who ever worked or associated with him, especially those of us in Pediatrics.

SURGERY

Pediatric surgeons generally are off our radar until we encounter a sick child with, or probably with, a surgical condition. We were fortunate to be adopted by a local pediatric surgeon in private practice when we began in 1961. Richard (Dick) Segnitz opened his practice in Lexington in August 1957 and was immediately caring for as many patients as time would allow.

A friend of mine recently told me of his experience with Dr. Segnitz. His oldest daughter, Linda, was delivered at term and immediately had a feeding problem. She would cough and gag whenever she was fed. The head nurse in the nursery, on her own, ordered chest x-rays, which led to Dr. Segnitz's being called soon afterward. The diagnosis was congenital tracheoesophageal (TE) fistula. The infant's family asked whether he had performed the corrective surgery before—"Yes, once." It didn't make the father comfortable when he saw Dr. Segnitz kneel and cross himself as he was on the way to the operating room. The incision was made in the midline of the upper abdomen.

When tiny Linda returned from the operating room, she had a gastrostomy for feeding. In the ensuing weeks, Linda underwent a series of esophageal dilations and eventual closure of the gastrostomy opening. Linda now lives in Orlando, Fla., and is seeking a new career in pharmacy.

Dr. Segnitz regularly came to our Pediatric Grand Rounds, and he even presented on occasion—but he never operated at University Hospital. In truth, he was shunned by our adult surgeons for violating an unwritten code. Segnitz had grown up in Milwaukee, Wis., graduated from Harvard Medical School, and served his pediatric surgical fellowship at Boston Children's Hospital. While at Boston Children's, he was awarded a Markle Fellowship, the highest honor a medical doctor in training or in his early years

Surgical team (left to right): Kara Cole, P.A.; Joseph A. Iocono, M.D.; Andrew R. Pulito, M.D.; Sean C. Skinner, M.D. Dr. Pulito retired as chief of Pediatric Surgery in March 2010 and was succeeded by Dr. Iocono.

could be given. Rather than remain an academic surgeon, however, Segnitz resigned his Markle Fellowship and went into private practice, first in Milwaukee, then in Lexington, where he was very successful. He needed to be, because he had 14 children.

In 1972, Dr. Segnitz had a major heart attack, an attack he survived but which kept him from ever returning to the operating room. He languished at home in Lexington until 1982, when he and his family moved to Culbertson, Mont., next to Saskatchewan and North Dakota. He worked part time as a general practitioner, progressively seeing fewer patients, until he closed his office in 1988. He died in 1993 at age 70.

About this time, Dr. George Pilling, one of the pediatric surgeons I had worked with while in training in Philadelphia, stopped in to say hello. He was in Lexington to inspect (in some official capacity) the pediatric surgery service that was just starting at UK.

Eventually, Dr. Ward Griffin recruited Robert Belin fresh out of training in Minnesota in 1970. I remember Dr. Wheeler's having Bob meet with our small department before he ever donned a scrub suit and his trying to pin Bob down to a specific schedule of seeing patients on the ward and reporting to him as the "chief." To myself, I kept saying, "Dr. Wheeler, back off, back off! We have waited too long to get a pediatric surgeon." Anyway, Bob kept his composure and made no promises. A couple of years later, Bob joined with Dorothy Hollingsworth, M.D., an endocrinologist in our department, in producing hypothyroidism in fetal lambs. The pathophysiology was not yet known for congenital hypothyroidism. In the experimental surgery lab he would operate on pregnant sheep, temporarily remove their fetus from the womb, and stitch the womb back together. He and Dorothy presented their findings at the Annual National Endocrine meeting.

In turn, Bob recruited Judah Jona to partner with him. They were not too busy, and the private pediatricians and others lured Dr. Belin to begin seeing patients they previously had been referring to Dr. Segnitz. Then Dr. Jona moved to Milwaukee Children's Hospital. This led to Andrew Pulito, M.D.'s coming to Kentucky, fresh out of his pediatric surgery fellowship at the Babies Hospital at Columbia University in New York City in 1978. Not long afterward, Dr. Belin resigned to work full time in his private practice, filling in Dr. Segnitz's niche. Andy soldiers on at University Hospital, where he is nearing retirement.

Along the way, Dr. Pulito has had two associates who are now in private practice elsewhere and currently has two associates at UK. In 2003, Dr. Joe Iocono, who trained at St. Christopher's Hospital for Children in Philadelphia, joined Pulito and became chief of Pediatric Surgery in 2010 as Pulito retired. Later, in 2008, Dr. Sean Skinner from the University of Oklahoma, joined the team, bringing valuable experience in laparoscopic techniques. The number of surgical procedures they performed last year was around 1600, if both scheduled and emergency cases are counted. Across Kentucky, children are in operating rooms every day; but, if the condition involves a newborn, the procedure is complicated or chancy, that patient is more likely than not being operated upon at University Hospital.

In addition to our three general pediatric surgeons, there are neurosurgeons, orthopedic surgeons, otolaryngology (ENT) surgeons, plastic surgeons, heart surgeons, and eye surgeons! Kentucky Children's Hospital now has a full complement of needed surgeons.

The most frequent pediatric surgery is for inguinal hernias on little boys, but significant other conditions include the following:

- Malrotation with medgut volvulus
- Intussusception
- Pyloric stenosis
- Hirschspring's Disease
- Torsion of an appendix testis
- Symptomatic anal fissure
- Perianal abscess/fistula in anus
- Congenital anomalies of many types
- Appendicitis

HEMATOLOGY–ONCOLOGY

My appreciation of hematology began on June 1, 1952, the first day of my junior year medical school clerkship. After 8 a.m., when the lab technicians had completed their phlebotomy rounds, the medical students were responsible for collecting the patients' blood and urine, taking the specimens to the basement lab just for medical students, and performing the initial complete blood count and urinalysis. Still trembling from having done a venipuncture on an elderly black man with a gummatous tertiary syphilitic chest aneurysm, I pulled up a stool to the work counter with microscopes, test tubes, and chemical bottles that stretched around the 20 x 20-foot room. There was a trim, mature woman in her white uniform, the supervising lab tech, who pointed to an open spot— she was to check and rescue me many times in the coming months.

First, I did the urinalysis, using test tubes, for dipsticks had not yet been invented, and specific gravity was done with a floating hydrometer, since the refractometer we now use had not yet been developed. Then on to the complete blood count (CBC). Next, I pipetted a thin column of anti-coagulated blood into a quartz tube with a chemical solution, then to a precalibrated colorimeter to show the hemoglobin concentration. Then I tried to count the numbers of various blood cells using a hemiacytometer (every student bought his own). It was a thick glass slide with gridded chambers of uniform depth into which precisely diluted suspensions of blood were placed. The numbers of cells in the chambers were counted, and, when combined with the known dilutions, the actual numbers of red blood cells and white blood cells per cubic milliter could be calculated. Finally, a Wright's stain blood smear on a glass slide was inspected under the microscope and the white blood cells were differentiated, counted, and recorded.

So, after about two hours, I was ready to take my data and return to the ward and record it on the clipboard at the foot of the bed. I was learning by doing—and I did get faster.

Twelve years later, as I began my work to change our central chemistry lab to automated microchemistries, I was amazed one day to see the brand new Coulter Counter—a sophisticated computer-driven electronic instrument that very accurately measured hemoglobin, the numbers of all the blood cells, as well as the red cell indices. Our chief laboratory technician, Denver Robertson, was testing it,

Phil Holland, M.D., hematologist.

particularly its speed. Previously, Denver had been the chief med tech at the Hazard Miners' Hospital and had held the record for speed in performing a CBC. This particular instrument effected an enormous advance in the care of all patients.

Before Jack Githens arrived in December 1960, he had hired a local lab technician, Lewis Newby, and had flown him to Denver to work in his research lab and learn the techniques he himself was using to perform bone marrow transplants on mice. In early 1961, Githens moved his Denver lab to a room on the MS corridor in our Medical Science Building. And in July 1961, his former fellow, Bill Hathaway, began setting up a coagulation research lab on the MN corridor, where he developed the reagents and methods to measure the known coagulation factors in blood. Thus, Hathaway was prepared when a child showed up with an unknown coagulation factor (See Chapter IV). Jack returned to Denver in June 1963, and Bill followed him a year later. The adult hematologists covered until Phil Holland, M.D., a newly minted pediatric hematologist, arrived a year later. Phil's focus was on childhood leukemia and cancer.

Importantly, Phil had a series of fellows—Curtis Abell, Claudia McEwen, Martha Greenwood, and John Geil—Greenwood and Geil are still carrying heavy clinical loads. They joined national collaborative clinical studies for their patients, so all received the standard of care for their unique oncological problems. After Hathaway left, the department depended upon the blood clotting section of the adult Division of Coagulation Disorders in the Department of Medicine for the next 30 years.

In September 1992, Vipul Mankad, M.D., vice chair of the Department of Pediatrics, University of South Alabama, Mobile, became our new chairman. Dr. Mankad was a

Martha Greenwood, M.D.,
Holland's first fellow.

Jack Geil, M.D., Holland's second fellow.

Bradley, age 6, with Jeffrey Moscow, M.D., was successfully treated for acute myelogenous leukemia, and now is in remission. Dr. Moscow's laboratory research involves the study of genes that regulate how anti-cancer drugs get into cancer cells.

pediatric hematologist whose research had been on sickle cell anemia. In addition to being our departmental chairman, he assumed the title of Head of Pediatric Hematology. But soon thereafter, he landed a new division head: Jeffrey Moscow, M.D.

As in other subspecialties, there has been a rapid evolution of their technology and science. Many hematologic diseases or conditions have been defined by biochemical and genetic mechanisms. Now, more than 80 percent of children with cancer can be cured, and leukemia is no longer necessarily a death sentence.

Dr. Moscow spent 12 years working in oncologic research at the National Institutes of Health in Bethesda, Md., before coming to Kentucky. Here for the past 12 years, he has continued his laboratory and clinical research while assembling a competent faculty of five additional pediatric hemotologists-oncologists.

Dr. John D'Orazio is a recent NIH grantee for the study of cellular factors that protect against developing melanoma.

Coagulation disorders in infants and children are now covered by two of the physicians.

Recently, Dr. Moscow opened a national study of relapsed leukemia. Dr. John D'Orazio secured a grant from the National Institutes of Health to further his studies on genetically determined malignancies. They all are part of the Children's Oncology Group sponsored by the National Cancer Institute. The Hemophilia Treatment Center finished 2008 with 71 children in its care.

NEPHROLOGY

Pediatric nephrology in Kentucky began with the arrival in 1963 of Dr. Nancy Holland and her husband, Dr. Phil Holland, from Cincinnati Children's Hospital. She had been a trainee of Dr. Clark West, whom I knew as the perpetual secretary of the American Pediatric Society. He was always on the podium at the national spring meetings. West, now in his late 80s, is still in the lab at Cincinnati Children's. Holland and West were the first to describe membranoproliferative glomerulonephritis (MPGN), a disorder of the kidneys.

Nancy Hinkle Holland, M.D., was the first native Kentuckian, along with her husband, hematologist Phil Holland, M.D., to be on the pediatric faculty.

Stefan Kiessling, M.D., is the current chief of Pediatric Nephrology. He is German educated and American trained.

The nephrology subspecialty in America traces its origin to insights into fluid and electrolyte balance, acid-base physiology, potassium, and other divalent mineral needs originally investigated by Drs. Gamble, Darrow, and others, in the 1940s and 1950s. Like other subspecialties, the discipline was advanced by significant uses of new treatments and diagnostic technologies—ACTH and glucocorticoid therapy for nephrotic syndrome in the 1950s, per cutaneous renal biopsy for glumerulonephritis in the 1950s, peritoneal dialysis in infants in the 1960s, followed by hemodialysis in children later in the decade. About 1970, we were visited by a surgical-medical team from the Medical College of Virginia in Richmond, who told us about their first kidney transplants in adults. We soon followed, and Dr. Phil Holland did the medical management of the first kidney transplant at the University of Kentucky. Eventually, the sub-board of pediatric nephrology was instituted in 1974, with the pediatric nephrologist Dr. Wallace McCrory at Philadelphia Children's Hospital as chairman. The discipline soon was firmly established.

All the while, Dr. Holland covered the pediatric renal service alone. In time, shortly before she retired, she got some help when Beth Jackson, who did her pediatric residency in Pittsburgh and pediatric nephrology fellowship in Cincinnati, came on board. Beth, in turn, received some relief from 24/7 on-call when another Cincinnati Children's renal fellow joined her, only to leave for general pediatric private practice after six years. Next, Randy Jenkins, M.D., came to help Beth, but he soon left for greener pastures at the University of Louisville. Then Beth again tapped the Cincinnati Children's pipeline for nephrologists. I sometimes wondered if Clark West was getting tired of stocking UK with nephrologists.

Next came Jens Goebel, M.D., who was energetic and focused on research. He became frustrated by the large clinical load's diverting his research energy and time, and returned to Cincinnati Children's, where he is currently the medical director of kidney transplantation and related problems. Soon after Jens left, Beth Jackson could not tolerate the lonely 24/7 clinical on-call responsibilities and returned to Cincinnati Children's, where she manages infants and children with obstructive and functional uropathies.

To rebuild our Division of Pediatric Nephrology again, we are indebted to Dr. Heinrich Werner, the interim chairman in 2003, when he recruited Stefan Kiessling, M.D., who was finishing his pediatric nephrology fellowship at Boston Children's

Hospital. Kiessling started July 1, 2003, with his wife as a professor in Rehabilitative Medicine, a package-deal. Pediatric nephrology has thus been resurrected at the University of Kentucky.

In Dr. Kiessling's short time at UK, he has been able to recruit additional staff, including Aftab Chishti, M.D., and develop a team of nurses, so is thus able to enlarge their clinical output. He is also involved in several clinical investigations. A significant study, in collaboration with cardiologist Carol Cottrill, is treating very young children with nephrogenic hypertension and a variant nephritic syndrome.

Dr. Kiessling points out that the kidney can no longer be thought of as a simple filter—it is also an endocrine/hormonal organ involved in hypertension and erythropoletin secretion. The major concern is the widening gap in the availability of kidneys for renal transplantation. Dr. Kiessling reports that nationwide there are more than 80,000 people, including children, awaiting a kidney transplant.

ENDOCRINOLOGY

Endocrinology evolved from descriptions of untreated patients whose condition could be traced back to hyperplastic or hypoplastic glands (pituitary, thyroid, adrenal, ovary, testis). Measurements of their secretions were non-specific in serum, *e.g.* protein-bound iodine (PBI) or butanol-extractable iodine (BEI) as an index of thyroid hormone

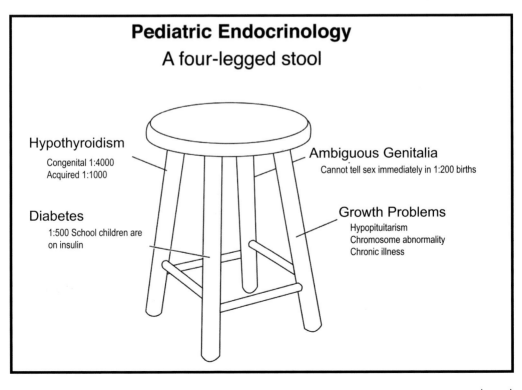

Pediatric Endocrinology
A four-legged stool

Hypothyroidism
Congenital 1:4000
Acquired 1:1000

Ambiguous Genitalia
Cannot tell sex immediately in 1:200 births

Diabetes
1:500 School children are
on insulin

Growth Problems
Hypopituitarism
Chromosome abnormality
Chronic illness

concentration. Other hormone estimates were made by measuring their derivatives in urine, such as 17-ketosteroids for total androgens or 17-ketogenic steroids for corticoids. Glucose in blood or urine was an indicator of insulin secretion by the B-cells of the pancreas.

Like other subspecialties, rapid advancement in understanding a patient's condition was made possible by the ability to measure individual hormones in the blood. Initially, this was done with bioassays. For instance, as late as the 60s, to measure the pituitary secretion of follicle-stimulating hormone (FSH), virgin mice were injected with extract from the patient's blood, a specified time allowed to lapse, then they were sacrificed and their ovaries weighed. These weights were compared to the ovarian weights in a group of control mice. There was a severe limit of the number of tests that could be done. Labor-intensive, to say the least.

Fast forward to 1958, when Drs. Solomon Berson and Rosalyn Yalow developed the radioimmuno assay for insulin, using only a tiny amount of serum. This was a quantum leap ahead for endocrinology. A few weeks after their report, my mentors, Angelo DiGeorge and Victor Auerbach, and I drove from Philadelphia to New York to witness this advance. Drs. Berson and Yalow graciously showed us and another small group the ins and outs of the insulin radioimmuno assay of insulin. They were working in the laboratory space of the recently deactivated Bronx Veterans Affairs Hospital. I noticed that Yalow had papers on her desk to start human growth hormone radioimmuno assays. Another thing I remember was her telling me about taking her guinea pigs home on the subway to her apartment over the Christmas holidays to maintain their care. Their insulin antibodies were essential to Berson's and her studies. She measured the areas

under each test recording peak with a hand-held protractor, a lengthy maneuver.

Radioimmuno assays for all the hormones were developed, making all the human hormones easily and rapidly measured, most with automated methods. This scientific advance has made endocrinology a viable clinical specialty.

Lawson Wilkins established the first pediatric endocrine clinic at the Harriet Lane Home, Johns Hopkins, in Baltimore in 1935. Subsequently, a

Dr. Rosalyn Yalow in 1977 became the second female Nobel laureate in Medicine. Together with Solomon Berson, she developed the radioimmuno assay technique. *Source: Michigan State University Department of Chemistry.*

similar clinic at Massachusetts General Hospital was set up by Nathan Talbot in 1942. The first diabetic clinic was set up by Elliott Joslin and Priscilla White, also in Boston. From these clinics, the second generation of pediatric endocrinologists came, all setting up both subspecialty care clinics and training programs. I am a third generation pediatric endocrinologist; there are several generations below me now.

Once I got to Kentucky, the first endocrine patients I saw were in traveling clinics. Most of the endocrine patients were children with diabetes mellitus, a nightmare for local family practitioners to manage in the mountains. Soon there were, on average, two children admitted each week in diabetic ketoacidosis. Blood glucose home monitors had not yet been developed, so we collected 24-hour urines in four aliquots (8 a.m.-noon / noon-4 p.m. / 4 p.m.-midnight / midnight-8 a.m.). From them, we could tell where the child needed more or less insulin and then determine the proper adjustment of a.m. regular/NPH and p.m. regular/NPH. We also began to detect children with congenital hypothyroidism, but not before three to six months when some mental retardation had already been inflicted.

By the late 1960s, I thought of my pediatric clinic as four-pronged. Treatments were still imperfect because many hormone replacements were extracts from animal

Leslie Scott, Ph.D., ARNP, CDE, and three children with diabetes.

endocrine glands. In time, pharmaceutical companies began synthesizing human hormones, which were precise and clean. Pediatric endocrinology became more attractive, so subspecialty boards were offered. My sub-board certification is #133, with the number now approaching 1,500.

In 1970, when Bill Hollingsworth was recruited to be the next chairman of the Department of Medicine, he brought along his wife, Dorothy Hollingsworth, who was an adult endocrinologist. However, University nepotism rules would not permit her to be in his department, so I readily welcomed her in Pediatrics as a coworker. She was energetic and engaging, and with Dorothy, something was always happening. Her first interest was the thyroid gland, which led to several jointly published papers. I still had one foot in the laboratory, and it was her stimulation that led us to modify the radioimmuno assay for thyroid hormone (TH) and thyroid-stimulating hormone (TSH) to be used in newborn screening. This was adopted by the State Department of Health Laboratory for statewide screening for congenital hypothyroidism in 1980.

Dorothy left in 1976 when her husband resigned to head up the Department of Medicine at the Veterans' Affairs Hospital in San Diego, Calif.—he wanted to be a bedside doctor, not an administrator. Dorothy was replaced by Michael Stelling, M.D., when he completed his pediatric endocrinology fellowship at the University of Virginia. Mike was to be at Kentucky for the next 10 years (1978-1988). These years were to be heavy clinical years; the patient load led to the abandonment of the pediatric endocrinology research laboratory.

Stelling was replaced by Jackson Smith, M.D., from North Carolina. Jackson had been a medicine-pediatrics resident at Chapel Hill, University of North Carolina, with fellowship training in adult endocrinology. He was on board when I retired from full-time status in 1995 at age 65. I have not stopped seeing patients some 15 years later.

My official replacement, Katherine Thrailkill, M.D., came on board in 1997 from Duke University. Her main interest was juvenile diabetes mellitus. We had a very large diabetes patient population. In 1980, we had set up outreach traveling clinics, supported by the Chatlos Foundation, at Eastern Kentucky locations (Pikeville, Barbourville, Olive Hill, Booneville and Monticello), seeing patients quarterly. We treated those children (50) who had been admitted to University Hospital in 1979 from these areas. Amazingly, in the following year (1980), only two were readmitted in diabetic ketoacidosis or for other reasons. Eventually, these traveling diabetes clinics obtained steady funding from the Berea College Appalachian Fund; last year, the total was $25,000.

Not long after Thrailkill's arrival, she was instrumental in getting a former Duke associate, John Fowlkes, M.D., to join the Endocrine Division. He arrived fresh out of post-doctoral training with his first NIH research grant pending. It came through. Our chairman, Vipul Mankad, renovated my old laboratory for him, and John was successful in his studies on growth hormone and proteases. After five years, however, John was recruited away by the University of Arkansas, Little Rock, and Katherine joined him a year later. They have succeeded in Little Rock.

All the while, Jackson Smith remained on station here in Kentucky and was named division chief. He says it was a battlefield promotion, when "the last man standing is in charge." Jackson recruited a young up-and-coming partner, Irene Hong-McAtee, M.D., who is making her way through the publish-or-perish academic system. But the Endocrine Division needs more faculty. The waiting time for a first-time Diabetes Clinic elective appointment is now six months. Some practicing physicians have figured out that the way to get a labor-intensive diabetic child off their hands is to get the child admitted to University Hospital—which gets the child sent directly to the Pediatric Diabetic Clinic for follow-up and continuation of care. Quite honestly, the newer "standards of care" for diabetic patients are extensive and beyond the capabilities and time required for a general pediatrician. In part, the division is employing a diabetes nurse-educator and two nurse practitioners. Even so hard-pressed, the staff of the Endocrine Division remains upbeat.

The care provided by the Traveling Diabetes Clinic, which provides care in the same location in Eastern Kentucky every three months, is best from the patient's point of view. In 2000, Fred D. Baldwin, a freelance reporter writing for the Appalachian Regional Commission (ARC), interviewed one of our Pikeville Clinic patients. An excerpt of his report in *Appalachia Magazine*, the *Journal of the Appalachian Regional Commission* reprinted here with permission, follows:

Going Where the Need Is

"The day Jason turned two years old," says Donna Hurley, "I cried all day. I was thankful that he'd lived to two."

Jason, her son, is 17 years old today and will be a high school senior this fall. At the age of 15 months he was diagnosed with Type 1 diabetes, which typically strikes children and teenagers. Every three months, he and his mother visit a health department clinic in Pikeville, Kentucky, for consultation with specialists from the Department of Pediatrics at the University of Kentucky College of Medicine in Lexington. For 30 years, its staff has conducted a traveling clinic to help families in Eastern Kentucky and nearby rural areas to manage a once-fatal disease.

Type 1 diabetes affects about one in 500 children and teenagers nationwide, according to the American Diabetes Association. Although no cure is known, the disease is manageable through careful attention to diet and regular injections of insulin. Before the discovery of insulin, diabetes was fatal; even now it remains the leading cause of blindness and kidney failure in adults.

Diabetes management is a demanding and never-ending process. Patients must check blood sugar levels several times per day. High or low levels are associated with everything from sluggishness (which affects school performance) to potentially fatal seizures. Hurley recalls many incidents like this in Jason's childhood.

"I'd be walking in the yard," she says, "and he'd be holding my hand and smiling. The next thing, he'd be passed out."

On the advice of her local physician, she made the four-hour drive to Lexington to consult with C. Charlton Mabry, M.D., at the University of Kentucky. As it happened, Mabry had already taken the lead in addressing the human and monetary costs of inadequate care for young diabetic patients.

"By the late 1970s," he recalls, "there were always one or two children in the (university) hospital with diabetes. They were almost always coming from Eastern Kentucky. We'd treat them and send them back to their primary care doctors. But they were bouncing back. Someone needed to see them more frequently."

In 1982, with financial support from private foundations, the university established traveling clinics to visit Eastern Kentucky counties using local facilities operated by the Kentucky Department for Public Health. Currently, the traveling doctors make quarterly visits to Pikeville and Barbourville, seeing about 100 patients at the sites. The university also operates a call-in service for patients three days a week during early morning hours, and twice a week in late afternoon.

ARC provided financial support during the 1989-1990 fiscal year. It did so again in 1997 with grants for specialized testing equipment and for providing clinics with computers and software to enhance the ability of patients to analyze self-collected data on their own blood sugar levels, an important element in diabetes management. The ARC funds also enabled the development of an extensive continuing medical education course on the pediatric management of Type 1 diabetes. Some 150 doctors and other health care professionals participated, making it the best attended of the university's outreach programs.

The university's original program goals were to produce measurable improvement in the clinical indicators of the disease, to reduce sick days and school absences, and to reduce the need for homebound schooling. The first goal was the key to the others, and meeting it depended on impressing patients with the absolute necessity of careful self-monitoring.

After the first year of operation, Mabry recalls, the Department of Pediatrics checked the hospital admission records of roughly 100 children participating in the traveling clinic program. Fifty of the children were hospitalized for treatment the year before the clinic began; only two were hospitalized the year after.

"I remember those numbers so vividly," Mabry says, "and then thinking, 'We've got to keep doing this!'"

That's harder and harder financially every year. Kathryn Thrailkill, M.D., chief of pediatric endocrinology and the current director of the traveling clinic, keeps handy "for the insurance companies" a folder of journal articles citing clinical data demonstrating that patients' blood sugar levels are far more likely to remain within an acceptable range when they get help four times a year, compared with only once or twice a year. This in turn can reduce the incidence of complications, meaning kidney failure or severe vision problems, by 50 to 70 percent.

"What's involved isn't a lot of high-tech," says Thrailkill, "but education."

In the last year she kept records, Donna Hurley spent about $8,600 of her own money on Jason's treatment, so she understands medical economics. She also has no doubt that the education she and Jason have received through the traveling clinics has been, and remains, a matter of life-and-death for him. His father died from diabetes complications about two years ago. With a catch in her voice, Hurley recalls how Mabry sought out Jason, then age 15, and told him in no uncertain terms, "This isn't going to happen to you!"

Though Dr. Thrailkill has long since moved, funding for the clinics, however financially and personally beneficial, remains a problem.

PULMONOLOGY

Cystic Fibrosis

Since antiquity, the problem of lung infections has been of great concern as well as activity in all of medicine—tuberculosis, asthma, diphtheria, pneumonia from any cause, abscess, emphysema, hyaline membrane, and other disorders. Pulmonology as a specialty owes its beginning to our ability to look at lung problems directly—through the bronchoscope.

When I was a beginning pediatric resident, my second rotation was the nursery service at Temple University Hospital in Philadelphia. There the nursery was housed in the former operating suites of the world-famous bronchoscopist, Dr. Chevalier Jackson. Around the high ceiling, in numerous matted frames, were objects that he had removed from the bronchi, throats, and lungs from people all over the world. His bronchoscopes were rigid, lighted, metal tubes of all sizes, diameters, and lengths. Though Jackson was an ear, nose, and throat surgeon, his work set the stage for pulmonology as a specialty.

Jamshed Kanga, UK's first pediatric pulmonologist, now leads a division of four faculty members.

Next came the flexible (fibro-optic) bronchoscope, allowing use by non-surgeons, and the development of the subspecialty of adult pulmonology, to be followed by pediatric pulmonology, as the flexible bronchoscopes were made smaller and smaller. Neonatal lung disease has become the province of the neonatologists, so the field of pediatric pulmonology now relates to intensive care and acute and chronic pulmonary diseases. They are regularly consulted on any ventilator-dependent child.

In the 1970s, a few self-declared pediatric pulmonologists began training younger pediatricians. Our first pediatric pulmonologist, Jamshed Kanga, M.D., studied under Dr. William Waring at Tulane in New Orleans. Dr. Kanga joined us in Kentucky in 1983, and the first certification exams were offered in 1986.

Even though a pediatric pulmonologist can offer essential advice and care for a variety of lung diseases and disorders, the patients that are their almost exclusive turf are those with asthma and with cystic fibrosis (CF)—or any patients requiring frequent clinic visits and frequent, lengthy hospitalizations. Prior to Kanga's arrival in 1983, the CF clinic had 50 patients and irregular care; the CF service now cares for more than 230 patients from all over our half of the state. With optimal care, many are surviving into adulthood. Probably the oldest survivor in Kentucky is our 52-year-old daughter, and though her lifestyle has been altered, she still enjoys life and managing her household. The more challenging patients are referred to UK.

At the time of our daughter's birth, the life expectancy of a CF patient was five years. When Dr. Kanga arrived, the median age of survival of a CF patient was 18 years; now it is 38. Today, emphasis is on early detection and early and aggressive treatment. About one-third of our patients have aged out of the pediatric age-range, so the CF service is currently a med-peds service. To provide for these patients, additional faculty have been hired as they have finished their training:

- Michael Anstead, M.D.—adult CF, asthma—fellowship at University of Kentucky
- Don Hayes, Jr., M.D.—asthma, CF, lung transplants—fellowship at University of Wisconsin

- Zoran Danov, M.D.—CF, outreach clinics—fellowship at University of Wisconsin

When Kanga arrived, the CF clinic met two half-days a week; now the clinic runs all day five days a week. Then, the typical census of hospitalized CF patients was 10 to 15 children, as compared to five now—dramatically revealing the improvement in care. Still, cystic fibrosis remains a difficult and life-shortening illness.

The advancement of CF knowledge and understanding has been fostered by the Cystic Fibrosis Foundation, a national organization. It has funded research and standardized the care and certification of CF treatment centers. A major stimulus to interest in CF followed the identification and delineation of the gene for CF in 1989. Further research has identified modifications, alleles of the major form of the gene. Some of these alleles are associated with less-severe forms of CF.

In 2005, with the introduction of expanded newborn screening in Kentucky, CF became one of the diseases added to the existing short panel. Dr. Kanga reports that 13 new CF patients began in clinic in 2009, all but two through the newborn screening program. If CF patients can be identified before secondary *pseudomonas* infection inevitably develops, the quality and duration of their lives can be improved.

The CF service requires a team approach. Standouts have been the lead special nurse, Lois Craigmyle, and Bob Kuhn, pharmacist. I remember the sign: "WE WILL DO IT = LOIS WILL DO IT." Bob Kuhn began helping the CF clinic soon after it started in 1985. He assisted and guided the use of the many drugs and special antibiotics tried and studied over the years. The whole team participates in the annual day-long family conferences initiated in 1984. Although children are no longer allowed to attend (fear of infection) parents and children of CF families depend on the team all year. When the expanded newborn screening bill was hanging up on the inclusion of CF testing, a grandmother of a patient accompanied us to a visit with a key legislator, a friend of hers, in his hometown office—he heard us, and the bill passed 38-0 in the state Senate. Most recently, we have lobbied the State Health Department to change the newborn screening for CF to include DNA (40 alleles) to make the diagnosis on the first clinic visit so as not to require two or three visits

THE NAME: CF

The disease name, cystic fibrosis, was coined by Dr. Dorothy Anderson, an Australian pathologist, who found that the pancreas of the CF patient was scarred and cystic due to the obstruction in the duct system with tenacious mucous: the same phenomenon that occurs in the lung and precedes the process in the pancreas.

(Anderson DK: Cyotic fibrosis of the pancreas and its relation to celiac disease; a clinical and pathologic study. Am J Dis Child 56: 344-399, 1938.)

for accurate confirmation of the diagnosis. The health department has accommodated us even though it is making draconian cuts in other parts of its budget.

Here in Kentucky, a former CF nurse entered the Kentucky Heritage Quilt Society challenge to create a quilt inspired by the theme "Stop and Smell the Roses." As a part of the 1999 Challenge Quilts contest, the winner, *Sixty-Five Roses,* has been displayed in museums, galleries, schools, and quilt shows in four states and viewed by more than 20,000 people, bearing a message of hope and inspiration.

About 65 Roses [(R)]

"65 Roses" is what some children with cystic fibrosis (CF) call their disease because that is, at first, what they think they are hearing.

Mary G. Weiss became a volunteer for the Cystic Fibrosis Foundation in 1965 after learning that her three little boys had CF. Her duty was to call every civic club, social and service organization seeking financial support for CF research. Mary's 4-year-old son, Richard, listened closely to his mother as she made each call.

After several calls, Richard came into the room and told his Mom, "I know what you are working for." Mary was dumbstruck because Richard did not know what she was doing, nor did he know that he had cystic fibrosis. With some trepidation, Mary asked, "What am I working for, Richard?" He answered, "You are working for 65 Roses." Mary was speechless.

He could not see the tears running down Mary's cheeks as she stammered, "Yes, Richard, I'm working for 65 Roses."

Since 1965, the term "65 Roses" has been used by children of all ages to describe their disease. But, making it easier to say does not make CF any easier to live with. The "65 Roses" story has captured the hearts and emotions of all who have heard it. The rose, appropriately the ancient symbol of love, has become a symbol of the Cystic Fibrosis Foundation.

65 Roses [(R)] is a registered trademark of the Cystic Fibrosis Foundation.

65 ROSES [R] **QUILT.**

Made of cotton fabrics and batting, the quilt measures approximately 50 x 50 inches, is machine pieced and quilted, has both machine and hand appliqué, and hand embroidery. The hexagons, a very traditional quilt shape, contain 64 roses. The 65th rose is held in the right hand. In the left hand is a dandelion, its seeds being scattered by the breath of life, representing the hope for a cure.

This framed quilt, created by a former CF clinic nurse, Carol Crabtree, RN, is now behind glass outside of the CF clinic, with permanent mounting scheduled in the near future in the new University of Kentucky Hospital after it opens in 2011.

Asthma

Dr. Mike Anstead reports that the division had about 3,000 visits to the peds pulmonary clinics in 2009 for asthma. Who were these wheezers?

One group comprises survivors of neonatal lung disease. The lung is perhaps the most immature organ in a prematurely born baby, but artificial ventilation, development of laboratory techniques for measuring blood gases, and Mary Ellen Avery's pioneering work on surfactant and its use in treating respiratory distress syndrome (hyaline membrane disease) salvaged these babies, but left many with bronchopulmonary dysplasia. The residual structural lung and respiratory tree damage leaves these infants with chronic airway hyper responsiveness and asthma. Another small group includes survivors of pediatric intensive care, older children who have required mechanical ventilation for whatever reason.

However, the principal group is made up of atopic children, with chronic inhalant allergen sensitization, who have asthma that is difficult to manage. Some of these are referred by allergists and/or co-managed by allergists. However, the majority are pediatric patients, referred from general pediatricians or family practitioners, who have asthma recalcitrant to the usual therapy with inhaled steroids and B-agonists. Dr. Peter Wong, former head of our General Pediatrics Division, tells me that ever since the first clinical trial of albuterol in 1969 and safe inhaled steroid preparations in the mid-1970s, pediatricians have increasingly prescribed their use, delivered with inhalers. Moreover, he stated with some authority that after antibiotics, asthma inhalers are the most frequent prescriptions that a general pediatrician writes, perhaps 25 percent of the total prescriptions.

I was astounded to hear this and to learn about the steady increase in childhood asthma over the past several decades. It is estimated that 250 million people worldwide have asthma. However, it has yet to be explained why it is most prevalent in large U.S. cities and least prevalent in third-world countries.

>< ><

When I started getting information together for this history, I asked a friend at a local retirement home who was the pediatrician for her three children and the same for other women at the home. Retirement home folks remember these things extremely well. One of her table-mates praised Dr. Richard Elliott lavishly for the time he responded to her mother's call for help as she, a young girl, was having an asthma attack. Elliott came to the house immediately, and she recalled his administering injections, probably long-acting adrenalin. There wasn't much else available then. She was rescued, and she remembered.

My first encounter with asthma occurred in 1953 as a junior medical student at Grady

Hospital in Atlanta. My medical school roommate, Harvey, came in wide-eyed after a night on duty on the White Men's Medical Ward. The story unfolded about a middle-aged man who had been admitted with severe bronchial asthma in the afternoon and had been receiving an intravenous drip of theophylline for hours, yet had not obtained relief. It was getting on up into the night and he and his junior medical resident physician didn't know what to do. In the stairwell they encountered Dr. Osler Abbott, a young but highly respected chest surgeon. Cardiothoracic surgery had not yet evolved. They told Dr. Abbott of their dilemma with the asthma patient.

Dr. Abbott thought for a minute, then commented that wheezing pre-op patients usually calmed down under ether anesthesia. But how could we give nasal-oral ether to our asthmatic? Abbott suggested they try by enema—it would bubble up through the lungs. The three separated.

The two looked at each other—then set off to the OR where they found a metal can of anesthesia ether. From this they filled a quart enema can with ether-water and administered it via rectal tube to the gasping, unresisting patient. Over the next half hour his breathing returned to normal!

Exhausted from his ordeal, while sitting on a bedpan in his bed to expel the enema, he reached for his cigarettes and matches. With cigarette between his lips, he lit it—and began to relax even more. While on the pan, he flicked cigarette ashes into the bedpan. KABOOOOM!!! He came flying through the curtains in the sitting position—landing on the floor in the middle of the ward. CHAOS! Nurse Cratchet was stunned, but flew into action. Harvey and his resident helped put things back in order—put the patient, with all hair singed off his bottom, back into bed, but with renewed asthma attack. They restarted the theophylline drip. A patient two beds down had a second heart attack. When the Atlanta Fire Department arrived, all was quiet. The only official record of the incident was a listing of fire department runs in the *Atlanta Constitution.* At our 50th class reunion, this was the most popular retelling. What we learned was that experimental medicine had to be more carefully thought out—thank God for the lack of medical malpractice in the 1950s.

My next lesson in asthma treatment took place in 1956 as a U.S. Navy doctor stationed with the Marines at Courthouse Bay, Camp Lejeune, N.C. After sick call at my infirmary on the beach, I would go up to the Base Hospital and co-attend with its pediatrician, Dr. Jack Rhoads. One afternoon, five-year-old Billy was admitted with acute bronchial asthma. He could suck air in, but he couldn't push it out—a short gasp and a prolonged effort to exhale. There was panic in his eyes, and he was placed in an oxygen tent. Dr. Rhoads checked his current *Pediatrics* journal for an article he had just read and sent for an ampule of ACTH (steroid). The ACTH was added to an IV, and Billy continued to struggle in the oxygen tent.

When I left at 5 o'clock, I wasn't sure Billy would make it through the night. But when I returned the next day, Billy was flashing around the ward on a tricycle, seeming no worse for the wear of yesterday. Our new intervention worked and the nurses removed the tent.

Treatment of acute asthma since the 1940s has progressed through numerous treatments:

Inhaled adrenergic agents such as isoprenaline and injections of long-acting adrenaline ⅢⅢ➤

Intravenous bronchodilating agents such as theophylline ⅢⅢ➤

Inhaled albuterol, a B-agonist or similar agents ⅢⅢ➤

Inhaled steroid preparations

We now recognize asthma as a chronic inflammatory lung disease. Pulmonologists have various treatment regimens to control mild intermittent asthmatics, mild persistent, moderate persistent, and the severe persistent cases, all involving ongoing medical supervision. The principal component to all these treatment regimens is inhaled corticosteroids. The availability and appropriate usage of inhaled corticosteroids in asthma has markedly improved asthma control and reduced mortality from asthma in children. About one out of every 10 children has asthma, making it the most prevalent chronic condition of children nationally. The prevalence rate of asthma in Kentucky is even higher than the national average. Locally we talk about the asthma belt of the Ohio River valley, and all Kentucky pediatricians will have to remain very familiar with asthma for the foreseeable future.

GASTROENTEROLOGY AND NUTRITION

Feeding of infants and children has always been a prime concern of pediatricians, but this subspecialty did not get started until the 1960s, when small intestinal biopsy for diagnosis and parenteral nutrition became feasible. The first child to undergo an oral duodenal biopsy at University of Kentucky Hospital was Robert H., whose case history is reported in Chapter II. The Rubin tube, which has a single small port (2.5 mm) at the end of the double-lumen tube, was safer for use in infants and small children than the original double-port (5mm x 2) Crosby capsule. Robert proved to have gluten-sensitive celiac disease.

Next, we were joined by Joyce Gryboski, M.D., a pediatrician interested in the newly appreciated problem in infants of various sugar intolerances. She was with us for two years while her husband was training in cardio-thoracic surgery. At one time, she chaired the first pediatric gastrointestinal subsection at the annual meeting of the Society for Pediatric Research. And, still later, she wrote a text describing the gastrointestinal problems confined to infancy (Gryboski J: Gastrointestinal Problems in the Infant. Major Problems in Clinical Pediatrics, Vol XIII. WB Saunders, Philadelphia, 1975.)

Here at Kentucky, Dr. Wheeler's general pediatricians were on their own until Joe Burke, M.D., completed his general pediatrics residency at UK, then spent the next two years as a pediatric gastroenterology fellow under William Shubert, M.D., at Cincinnati Children's Hospital. He was welcomed by Dr. Wheeler when he returned to our faculty as pediatric gastroenterologist.

Joe was a quiet clinician who listened and took a careful history before doing his physical examination. I was greatly impressed when he made the correct diagnosis of pancreatitis on my 10-year-old daughter who, much later, was found to have cystic fibrosis. The following day, her serum amylase was found to be greatly elevated. Joe did not have any laboratory skills, and with our relatively small patient population at the time, most of his work continued in general pediatrics. Two years later, he began a conventional diagnostic radiology residency here at UK, after which he practiced diagnostic radiology in Lumberton, N.C.

One of Dr. Noonan's early faculty recruits was Sam Kocoshis, M.D., who had just completed his pediatric gastroenterology fellowship at Yale under Dr. Joyce Gryboski. Sam's early research centered on bile acids, and he had the necessary laboratory skills to pursue this interest during his several years in Kentucky. Sam eventually ended up at Cincinnati Children's Hospital's GI Division, where he is a full professor and co-director of the Pediatric Nutrition and Intestinal Care Center as well as medical director of the Small Bowel Transplantation Program. I remember that Sam's wife personally thanked Dr. Noonan for finding Sam an office after he had been here for more than a year.

After a hiatus of several years, Dr. Noonan appointed an ex-resident, Bob Dillard, who had one year of pediatric GI training at Cincinnati. Bob stayed for several years doing clinical GI. After Dr. Mankad succeeded Noonan, Bob was unhappy. He went into private gastroenterology practice at Sacred Heart Children's Hospital in Pensacola, Fla., and then subsequently moved to Louisville. He has remained active in our school's Medical Alumni Association.

On the national scene, pediatric gastroenterology was emerging, empowered by advances in parenteral nutrition, safe pediatric ileocolonoscopy, percutaneous liver biopsy, improvement in pediatric surgery, and better understanding of various genetic and immunologic disorders. Again, a new face was recruited to fill this void in our department.

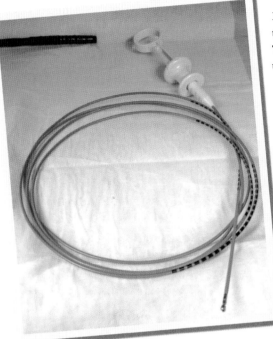

Biopsy forceps used to obtain mucosal tissue specimens during endoscopy. The directed specimens are obtained under endoscopic visualization.

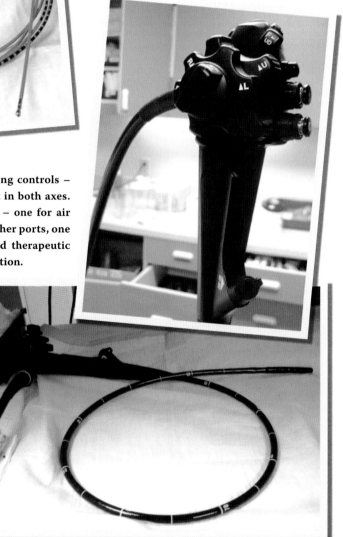

The head end of the endoscope showing controls – fiberoptic endoscopes offer movement in both axes. There are three button head controls – one for air inflation and water spray. Of the two other ports, one permits passage of biopsy forceps and therapeutic equipment, and the other provides suction.

The flexible upper endoscope is used to perform diagnostic and therapeutic endoscopy of the upper gastrointestinal tract; smaller fiberoptic endoscopes available now permit evaluation even in the smallest infants.

Mankad recruited Harohalli Shashidhar, M.D., who was just finishing his GI fellowship at Tufts New England Medical Center, Boston. His quiet manner, coupled with an excellent GI knowledge-base, has made him popular with an ever-growing clinic population. "Shashi" in turn attracted one of our own graduates, Deborah Flomenhoft, M.D., to train in both adult and pediatric gastroenterology and to join our faculty.

In 2004, Shashidhar's clinic was brightened up by the hire of our new Medical School dean, Jay Perman, M.D., a pediatric gastroenterologist. Dr. Perman began seeing patients with Shashi and staff on a part-time basis. Each Thursday that Dr. Perman is in clinic, he brings along extra medical students, thus creating a busy, congested work station—but all benefit. The GI team has begun to see some patients at outreach clinics and in a young adult clinic. We recently learned that Dr. Perman is soon leaving to become a college president in Maryland.

DENTISTRY

The need for pediatric dentistry became apparent just after University Hospital opened. A toddler with hemophilia fell and tore the lip attachment above his teeth and gums. He was administered fresh frozen plasma, the only treatment available at the time, which induced clot formation. When he went home, he would injure it again, and the prolonged bleeding would require readmission and another infusion of plasma.

After several readmissions, we asked John Mink, D.D.S., our only pediatric dentist, to help us. He made an impression of the toddler's mouth and teeth, then fabricated a denture that would protect the area and cemented it onto the teeth. He left this special denture on for about three weeks until the area healed completely. This scenario occurred several time until the child's gait was sturdy.

Over time, the pediatric dental faculty and their residents grew in number and availability. Not only are they involved with children with bleeding disorders, but they also provide dental operative care to our handicapped patients with special needs— frequently taking them to the operating room to perform extensive dental restorations.

Our pediatric dentists are necessary members of the cleft palate team led by a plastic surgeon. They make and provide palate devices and perform customized major dental care for those children. Dr. John Mink, our original pediatric dentist, recalls

John S. Mink, D.D.S., M.S.D., chief of Pediatric Dentistry. Dr. Mink is now in his 48th year at UK.

the change from glass baby bottles to our current plastic baby bottles. Young children would sometimes fall with the bottle in their mouths with the resulting injuries. Now with plastic baby bottles, they can run all over the place, including sidewalks.

Much of their work has always involved preventive dentistry. Not infrequently parents put carbonated beverages, including Mountain Dew, in baby bottles. In school and office work, the pediatric dentist or his aides will paint children's teeth with a dye that attaches to plaque, have them rinse, then with a mirror show them the extensive plaque on their teeth. Then after brushing, the children are shown the residual plaque, the bacterial film that causes tooth decay. Our water supply is now fluorinated, but there is still much more to be done in dental care for children. One of their efforts is to operate a three-chair dental office on wheels, for the last 15 years targeting several drastically underserved Appalachian counties, where cavities in children are horrific.

Mink reports on the timing of dental care: "We like to see them really young, a year old or so, just to start trying to prepare parents with preventive procedures. Dental decay or problems is the No. 1 disease in children right now in the United States."

ADOLESCENT MEDICINE

Prior to the 1960s in Lexington, a large majority of a private practicing pediatrician's patients were infants and toddlers. A typical day in their life began by examining newborns delivered overnight and meeting their mothers. As Lexington grew and more pediatricians from our training program and other regional programs settled here, the shingles on their offices began to read "Pediatrics and Adolescent Medicine."

This label change occurred not only from increased competition, but also from societal changes in attitudes about adolescents. Of the 47 private practicing pediatricians currently listed in the telephone Yellow Pages, most advertise themselves as pediatric and adolescent doctors.

There has been recognition of a need to reduce the risk-taking behaviors of adolescents and a need to acknowledge that there are different sets of stresses, injuries, and illnesses in teenagers, resulting in the appointment of Earl Vastbinder, M.D., to the Department in the 1960s. Even with our relatively small clinic population at the time, Earl was kept busy working with teenagers' illnesses and special problems. After four years, Earl left for Nashville, where he joined the Vanderbilt pediatric faculty.

The next big push to help adolescents came when ex-governor Bert Combs served as the lead counsel for the poor school districts that won the Kentucky Supreme Court decision that the state's system of public school funding was unconstitutional. The Kentucky General Assembly reacted by passing the Kentucky Educational Reform Act (KERA). With KERA and more taxes came significant improvement of rural and mountain schools. Fayette County and other urban areas got very little of the money, with most

Hatim Omar, M.D., Chief of Adolescent Medicine, 1998, and patient.

going to the rural and mountain schools. Included in KERA was the requirement that all teachers be certified, one-room schools be abolished, and a student testing system be put in place to assess student progress every year. A Pike County wag once told me that KERA stood for Keep Everybody Running Around.

The part of KERA that affected our department was the creation of a Family Resource Center (FRC) at each public school. Each FRC had a volunteer board of directors to oversee the needs of the children. These board members were a real mixed bag, but they did make decisions about children with problems. These boards, generally, are the source of "school referrals" to our present-day Adolescent Medical Clinic. Last year's funding for these FRCs was $62.5 million.

The next effort in adolescent medicine from our department was to address the high rate of teenage pregnancies. In the late 1970s, Dr. Dorothy Hollingsworth had been the first faculty person to bring this to our attention, but she moved on to the University of California-San Diego, where she set up a comprehensive program to deal with teen pregnancies. Soon after Hollingsworth's departure, with state support, a section of the Division of General Pediatrics was designated the Young Parents' Program. The focus seemed to be on well-baby exams and immunizations, along with birth control to their mothers. But there was much more that needed to be accomplished.

In 1998, then-chairman Vipul Mankad made a good hire and appointment in Hatim Omar, M.D. Omar had been trained in pediatrics and in obstetrics/gynecology. He was certified in the new pediatric sub-board, Adolescent Medicine. In addition to the Young Parents Program, he began seeing adolescents with eating disorders, oncology issues, suicide potential, and any health-care need. Referrals are made by physicians, parents, teenagers themselves, and schools.

A study county in Central Kentucky, Lincoln, is showing the effect of the division's availability and care of troubled or sick teenagers. Adolescent medicine as now being practiced has been promoted by other subspecialties—endocrinology, gynecology, gastroenterology, infectious diseases, sports medicine, and other disciplines such as social work and clinical psychology. Certification by board exams began in 1994, and those specialists meet regularly with the national academic pediatric societies and have a rigorous program.

One issue the clinic is currently focused on, suicide, is the second-leading cause of death in Kentucky for this age group. Faculty make themselves available by email, telephone, or face-to-face when a troubled teen needs counseling or help. In Lincoln County, there have been fewer teen suicides since their program began, Omar said.

I wondered whether their staff is open to and dealing with sexual orientation problems. Five percent of males and three percent of females acknowledge their gay orientation by 18 and 25 years of age, respectively; their suicide rate is very high. But I was glad to hear a radio announcement that the division was holding a public meeting on teen suicide.

INFECTIOUS DISEASES

Today, March 1, 2010, a radio newsman announced the start of the 43rd annual Iditarod. This trail dog-sled race memorializes the March 1925 race of 1,200 miles to take diphtheria antitoxin from the last open-water port in Alaska—Seward—to the iced-in port of Nome on the Bering Strait. The citizens of Nome, mostly children, were dying—left and right—with diphtheria. Their stock of diphtheria antitoxin was exhausted and could not be replaced because of the 1924-25 winter isolation season. The daily telegraph reports from Alaska in the rescue mission kept the 48 down-under states electrified for days. Dogs and their mushers became heroes.

Almost all of the early writings and investigations in medicine were about infectious diseases, beginning with Hippocrates' description of a mumps epidemic in his first book, *Epidemics.* The invention of printing in the mid-15th century revived learning, and it is significant that the first printed works on children were about their infections.

Fast forward to American pediatricians, beginning with Abraham Jacobi. We can observe that all the leaders in pediatrics up until the most modern times made their marks and publications on infectious disease topics and problems. Here in Lexington, in the early part of the 20th century, the focus was on summer diarrhea and its link to the milk supply, as recorded in Chapter One.

When the College of Medicine was started, a long-time professor of bacteriology at UK, Morris Sherago, counted on and demanded to be appointed head of the Department of Bacteriology. Dean Willard recognized "Bugs" Sherago's grab for power and simply did not create a Department of Bacteriology. This created a major divide between the College of Medicine and main campus, a divide that lingers today.

But the University Hospital was saved, almost by accident. Col. Elon Tucker, a just-retired U.S. Army Medical Service Corps bacteriologist and his recently retired twin brother, moved into a house directly across the street from University Hospital. The large unoccupied house still stands on South Limestone Street in the shadow of our new 12-story University Hospital now under construction.

Colonel Tucker walked across Limestone and introduced himself to W.B. (Pete) Stewart, the chairman of the Pathology Department. Forthwith (1962), Pete made Colonel Tucker the head of the Central Clinical Laboratory's bacteriology section. Colonel Tucker brought military discipline and experience to the job. It so happened that Colonel Tucker angered a lot of surgeons because he would not make final reports until he had firmly identified the organism in question. However, if you came

Col. Elon Tucker, bacteriologist.

down to his lab, he would lay out the Petri dishes and discuss them with you. His game was the only one in town.

UK pediatricians learned fast to walk back to discuss infectious diseases with Colonel Tucker—after all, both were on the fourth floor. It became Dr. Warren Wheeler's practice to walk back to Tucker's lab every morning before Pediatric Morning Report at 8:30 a.m. Colonel Tucker would already have all the pediatric cultures laid out on the bench for discussion—he had been there since before 7 a.m. This way, Dr. Wheeler had a "leg up" before his residents and faculty made their reports.

Those infectious disease local experts who followed Dr. Wheeler—David Wilson and Bob Broughton—continued the practice of direct consultation with Colonel Tucker. Colonel Tucker retired in the 1970s, to be replaced by Norman Goodman, Ph.D., plus two other people—Sue Overman, a bacteriology Ph.D. and her husband, Tim Overman, M.S., now at our Veterans' Administration Hospital.

The modern era of pediatric infectious diseases began in the 1980s with advances based on new diagnostic modalities—DNA hybridization and sequencing, cloning, PCR, and other increasingly sophisticated molecular methods. While many classic infectious diseases have almost disappeared, the new activity is about opportunistic infections in the ever-increasing populations of immunocompromised patients: Lyme disease, Kawasaki disease, HIV/AIDS, MRSA, *c. difficile*, and others.

Those in the Infectious Disease subspecialty service of Kentucky have taken on diverse additional duties. Dave Wilson was our director of Inpatient Services in the 1970s and 1980s. He has moved on to various administrative positions at other institutions. Dr. Bob Broughton has assumed additional duties of pediatric resident recruitment and pediatric ICU service, where he is certified in Critical Care. Dr. Chris Nelson, who joined us in 1992 as our latest Infectious Disease subspecialist, is now doubling as the University Hospital and Kentucky Children's Hospital Director of Infection Control. All the hand-washing devices and stations throughout our hospitals are noticeable.

Another aspect of Infectious Disease subspecialty activity involves vaccines and their use; use responsibility falls to the General Pediatricians. Peter Wong, M.D., has shown leadership in this area. It is now recommended that all children have a series of 22 immunizations by their second birthday, as shown in the attached schedule.

New Vaccines and Recommendations

New vaccines appearing in guidelines developed by an expert panel of the Infectious Disease Society of America, and endorsed by the American Academy of Pediatrics, the National Association of Pediatric Nurse Practitioners, and the Pediatric Infections Diseases Society:

- Human papillomavirus vaccine;
- Live, attenuated influenza vaccine;
- Meningococcal conjugate vaccine;
- Rotavirus vaccine;
- Tetanus toxoid, reduced diphtheria toxoid, and acellular pertussis vaccine;
- Zoster vaccine.

New combination vaccines:

- Measles, mumps, rubella, and varicella vaccine;
- Tetanus, diphtheria and pertussis, and inactivated polio/Haemophilus influenzae type b vaccine.

Hepatitis A vaccines are now recommended universally for young children.

All children ages six months through 18 years and adults older than 50 should receive influenza vaccines.

Additionally, a second dose of varicella vaccine has been added to the routine childhood and adolescent immunization schedule.

Modern-day vaccines are quite effective, but some modern parents have chosen not to have their babies immunized—thinking that vaccines pose a greater risk than the illnesses.

IMMUNIZATION GUIDELINES FOR UK GENERAL PEDIATRICS
October 2009

Newborn	Hep B	#1		9 months	(catch up as needed)	
2 months	DPaT	#1*		12 months	Varicella vaccine #1	
	IPV	#1*			PCV7	#4
	HepB	#2*			HepA	#1
	HIB	#1*				
	PCV7	#1		15 months	MMR	#1
	RV	#1			DPaT	#4
					HIB	#4
4 months	DPaT	#2*				
	IPV	#2*		18 months	HepA	#2
	HIB	#2*			(HIB	#4?)
	PCV7	#2				
	RV	#2		19-47 months complete HepA series		
					(HIB	#4?)
6 months	DPaT	#3*				
	IPV	#3*		4 years	MMR	#2
	HepB	#3*			Varicella	#2
	HIB	#3*				
	PCV7	#3		5 years	DPaT	#5
	RV	#3			IPV	#4

DPaT ....Diphtheria, Pertussis, Tetanus
IPV ....Inactivated Poliovirus
HepB ....Hepatitis B
HepA.............Hepatitis A
HIB................Haemophilus influenzae type b
PCV7.............Pneumococcal
RV ....Rotavirus
MMR.............Measles, Mumps, Rubella

PHARMACY

My first appreciation of the pharmacist's role with children came with Harry Shirkey, R.Ph., in 1960. He argued that children in and out of the hospital rarely received the dose of a medication ordered for them. He made his point by showing us a series of slides. The most memorable image to me was that of a rambunctious toddler standing in his hospital crib with a red liquid medication vehicle all over his face, clothes, and crib bedding—how much of this teaspoon of medicine did he get?

We were fortunate in Kentucky that we were just starting and open to new and innovative ideas. Paul Parker, R.Ph., was the first director of Hospital Pharmacy. When we began in April 1962 with a small number of patients, we had bottles of liquid medications and jars of pills from a core, but limited, list of pharmaceuticals. These bottles and jars were actually at the nurses' station, along with teaspoons and tablespoons for doling out the medications from a pint of a liquid or a bottle of 100 tablets.

Then the doctors and nurses would say, "Oh, I need a dose of a certain medication for this patient, and I'll need a tablet of another medication for the next patient." They would put each in an unlabeled paper mini-cup and head to the patient's bedside, hoping that they wouldn't get interrupted or waylaid for something else. This mode of passing out medications, of course, could lead to frequent safety issues and errors.

This inconsistent and inexact method—but standard for the times—led to the adoption of the unit-dose system, our hospital being one of the first to do so. With the unit-dose system, written medication orders were sent to our Central Pharmacy, where a technician put each medication—liquid or tablet—in an individual container or envelope with the patient's name, room number, and date and time it was to be taken.

Next, the College of Pharmacy, which has a long history of excellence, teamed up with University Hospital and began assigning its faculty and students to work with our housestaff and clinicians. The first College of Pharmacy faculty member assigned to Pediatrics was John Pecora, who had a desk at the nurses' station. He attended morning report, made teaching rounds with the general pediatrics teaching rounds, and was available to the subspecialists.

Next, during the 1970s, our Central Pharmacy began preparing intravenous fluids with added electrolytes and medications as ordered. This was a big change, for doctors had traditionally prepared their own custom fluids and added the medications and drugs.

Dr. Pecora paved the way for a dedicated pharmacist to work with hospitalized pediatric patients. In 1985, Dr. Pecora moved on to be an assistant director of Central Pharmacy; today he is retired, but working in the College of Pharmacy alumni office. He was replaced by a pharmacist, Robert Kuhn, R.Ph, and Pharm.D., who had prior experience at Columbus Children's Hospital, Columbus, Ohio. Bob has enlarged

Dr. Robert Kuhn checks on a patient.

responsibilities for our hospitalized children, with a special interest in children with leukemia and with cystic fibrosis. Also, he developed the pediatric pharmacy residency program, the first trainees finishing in 1987. As the pharmacy services have expanded, the official name became Kentucky Children's Pharmacy Services. It now has staff with special expertise in neonatal medicine, hematology and oncology, respiratory disease, and cystic fibrosis.

Along the way, Bob Kuhn has become deeply imbedded in our Cystic Fibrosis Clinic, selecting the best antibiotic for use with individual patients and conducting clinical trials with new antibiotics. Dr. Kuhn tells me that he and others are working to see Pediatric Pharmacy officially recognized as a subspecialty.

GENETICS

Descriptions of the Genetic Clinics and Diabetes Clinics show sharp contrasts. Genetic Clinics focus on diagnosis and understanding, not treatment, whereas the Diabetes Clinics focus on direct continuity of care. Dr. Bryan Hall gives the history of the genetics services. A native Kentuckian, Dr. Hall tells his family story, now enmeshed with our Department of Pediatrics:

UK PEDIATRIC GENETICS—A HISTORY
By Bryan D. Hall, M.D.

My father, Dr. Lon C. Hall, was the first pediatrician to practice in Eastern Kentucky. His practice started in 1939 in Paintsville, Ky. At that time there were no antibiotics or scalp vein intravenous needles for children. Consequently, many of his patients with serious infections and dehydration died as he helplessly observed.

Even after antibiotics became available as well as infant scalp vein needles, there were still children that needed to be transferred quickly, which was difficult because of poor roads, unreliable transportation and far-away children's centers in Louisville and Cincinnati. Frustrated, he designed and had built a pediatric floor on the top level of the Paintsville Hospital in 1953, which he staffed and to which other doctors could admit their patients for care. It had 11 beds, a treatment room and a formula room. Each patient room had a child's bed and a bed for the mother.

He was ecstatic when the Albert B. Chandler University of Kentucky Hospital and Medical School were built. It meant he had a close referral center and an outstanding faculty to call for consultation.

The doctor he most frequently consulted with was Dr. Jacqueline Noonan, a pediatric cardiologist. Eastern Kentucky had an extremely high rate of congenital heart defects, and Dr. Lon was very interested in diagnosing and treating them if he was able. Dr. Noonan was quoted as saying, "When Dr. Lon referred a patient for cardiac evaluation and admission, you always knew that the child was sick and that the diagnosis was usually correct."

The support of the University of Kentucky Department of Pediatrics was so important to Eastern Kentucky physicians and the families they treated. A gradual decrease in infant mortality and an improved quality of life can, in part, be ascribed to the presence of the UK Department of Pediatrics and their inpatient services.

Genetics was not considered much of a practical specialty until the early 1970s. Generally, lay persons and many physicians still thought of genetics as a branch of laboratory research involving peas and fruit flies. Certainly, it could not be applied except in laboratories within the confines of hospitals or hospital-related clinics. However, the advent of chromosome and metabolic analyses, which began in earnest in the late 1960s, set the stage for children with potential genetic disease to be tested from blood and urine samples collected in faraway places and sent to the medical center. This, in turn, set the stage for the development of university-based genetic outreach clinics where a team of geneticists with support personnel could travel to far-removed sites and perform clinical evaluations on patients with possible genetic conditions and bring back blood and/or urine for genetic testing when indicated. This meant the families would not have to travel 100-plus miles to get state-of-the-art genetic services.

I helped start and run the first genetic outreach clinics in the world in 1972 while I was at the University of California-San Francisco. We saw more than 1,000 patients per year in these clinics, which were located as far north as Redding, Calif., and as far south as Visalia, Calif. We proved that it was cost-effective, but more importantly, we proved that when genetic services were available in the local community, 75 percent of the patients who we saw would not have traveled to the University of California-San Francisco for the same services.

Upon arriving at the University of Kentucky in July 1981, I started the preparations for outreach genetic clinics in Eastern Kentucky. I had already received a five-year federal grant to start outreach genetic clinics in Eastern Kentucky. Having been born and raised in Eastern Kentucky (Paintsville) and having eight relatives who were practicing physicians in Kentucky, the locals and the medical community considered me one of them. This was very important, for genetics at the time was considered associated with abortion, and Eastern Kentuckians being conservative and very religious were strongly against abortion. Had I been an outsider, I doubt I would have had any chance of getting the lay and medical communities' support for starting genetic clinics in their backyard.

Each potential outreach site was identified and I presented the outline of my genetic services via these clinics to interested lay persons, political office holders and county medical societies. We emphasized three things:

1. There would be no charge for families who had no way to pay;
2. We were not associated with abortion clinics or anyone doing abortions;
3. We would not get involved with administering medical care to these patients unless requested by the referring physician.

Both the referring physician and the family would receive a summary of our evaluation, and we would be available to discuss any questions either might have about our comments or suggestions. We would also give periodic educational lectures to requesting groups. Our clinics would be held either in ARH hospitals or the local health departments, although in recent times they are all held in health departments.

We got immediate approval for four sites, and by the end of the first year approximately nine sites were functional. After a few years, we were seeing between 300-350 patients per year, and the clinics were considered very successful by everyone involved. A total of more than 10,000 patients with birth defects and/or genetic disorders have been seen since 1982.

Our first clinic started in Somerset, and it is still going. We also have clinics in Ashland, Paintsville, Pikeville, Whitesburg, Corbin and Pineville. They occur every two to six months depending on the volume of patients. Our genetic outreach clinics are known throughout the country as one of the best and most expansive. Our patients have contributed greatly to the identification of new disorders and/or new information about established disorders. Since we take medical students, residents and visiting professors with us on these clinics, they represent a strong educational contribution as well.

One of our most remarkable genetic outreach clinics was held at the McRoberts Medical Clinic in October 1986. McRoberts is approximately 20 miles from Hazard, and it is at the end of the line with no road going farther. This clinic was held on a Saturday, and it was held in a school gymnasium, not a site where any previous genetic clinics had been held.

The stimulus for this clinic started some four months earlier when I saw a family whose 6-year-old son had been diagnosed by Dr. Jacqueline Noonan as having Marfan's syndrome. In taking an initial family history, it became obvious that this boy's mother and maternal grandmother also had Marfan's. Even more surprising was that 40 relatives over five

MARFAN SYNDROME

Marfan syndrome is characterized by clinical variability with cardinal features occurring in three systems:

1. Skeletal – Increased height, disproportionately long limbs and digits, joint laxity, and scoliosis.

2. Eyes – subluxation of the lenses, myopia.

3. Heart – mitral valve prolapse, dilation of the aortic root, dissection of aorta with rupture.

The basic defect lies in the connective tissue, collagen.

generations also had Marfan's syndrome. This was just one branch of the family! Further calls to members of five other branches of the family suggested an additional 60 individuals might also have Marfan's.

It became obvious that this entire family needed further evaluation, but it would take months of preparation. Logistics were potentially complicated, but luckily most family members lived within a 25-mile radius of McRoberts. Locals (i.e. physicians, nurses, lay public) had always known there were a lot of people with "Marfan's syndrome" or

MARFAN Expedition was a one-day foray into Eastern Kentucky by a large team of specialists, residents, and students to examine more than 135 people, most from one family, having or suspected to have Marfan syndrome. The study led to the identification of the causative gene. The gene is on the proximal portion of the 15th chromosome at 15q 21.1 and called fibrillin. The pedigree of the family is shown on page 155.

some lethal genetic heart problem, but no one had connected all the different family branches.

Marfan's syndrome is a common (1 in 5,000) condition involving abnormal connective tissue, which can result in sudden death due to a dissecting aortic aneurysm. Individuals with Marfan's tend to be tall and thin and often have long, narrow fingers, dislocated lenses of the eye with nearsightedness, chest deformation and scoliosis. It is inherited as an autosomal dominant, which means a single abnormal gene manifests the above features in an affected individual, and 50 percent of that person's offspring are at risk of getting the abnormal gene and, thus, showing manifestations of Marfan's syndrome. It does not have an adverse effect on mentality or fertility. The condition can have serious body-image problems. In 1986, the gene for Marfan's syndrome had not been identified, so we knew that this family, because of the large number of affected individuals, offered a unique opportunity to discover the causative gene.

We had no grant to pay for such a huge undertaking unless we could get critical people to volunteer for a full-day clinic. Plus, equipment such as slit lamps for eye examinations and an echocardiogram machine for heart anatomy would have to be lent out free. We needed an ophthalmologist for eye evaluation and a cardiologist for heart examination. Johns Hopkins University in Baltimore was contacted to see if they were interested in doing gene studies on the patients. Dr. Reed Pyeritz of Hopkins agreed to come and participate in the clinical evaluations as well as take blood samples back to the molecular lab for analysis. A total of 14 professionals (four residents, two medical students, two genetic counselors, three geneticists, one cardiologist, one ophthalmologist, one genetic secretary) donated their services. We arranged for a family reunion with lunch to be held in the local gymnasium while we were to see patients at the nearby McRoberts Medical Clinic. The clinic was advertised in the local media, and each family member was notified. We had no idea that more than 135 people would show up, some even not family members who heard there was a "free" clinic. These non-family members had a relative who was tall and thin and/or had one or more of the additional features found in Marfan's syndrome.

Most of us drove up the evening before and stayed at La Citadel Motel in Hazard. Besides the usual collegial conversation, we planned

MARFAN PEDIGREE

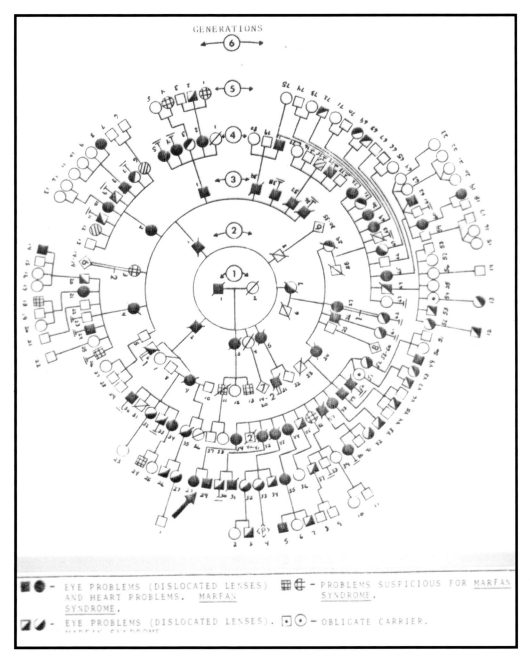

additional last-minute strategies for the next morning that began at 9 a.m. The local health department and McRoberts clinic nurses were set up for us when we arrived. There were already a cadre of patients there. Each patient had a history, pedigree, numerous measurements, complete physical, slit-lamp exam, echocardiogram and blood drawn. Many also had photographs taken. All were given counseling relative to the findings with follow-up to be determined after molecular testing was completed. Recommendations would follow afterward. We finished around 7 p.m. and headed back to Lexington, all exhausted but intellectually energized. The total cost of the clinic was $1,200, which our genetic grant could handle. In 1986, such a clinic with all the tests would have cost more than $100,000 had not everything been donated.

We made history that day as we identified more than 100 individuals from one family group who had Marfan's syndrome by exam, pedigree analysis and/or history. This was four times the number of Marfan's individuals in one family ever reported. We were also able to clearly show how variable the clinical manifestations could be in the same family.

It would take an additional six months to complete and send out all the summaries for each patient seen. We later learned that our family contributed to the identification of the gene for Marfan's syndrome. The gene was called fibrillin, and it was on the proximal portion of the 15th chromosome at 15q21.1 (*Genomics* 9:355-361, 1991). The gene test is now readily available and is accurate in more than 95 percent of the cases.

The UK Department of Pediatrics Genetic Service continues to identify the gene for many disorders including sex-linked mental retardation, ectodermal disorders, skeletal disorders and multiple congenital anomaly syndromes. Chromosome disorders are also being regularly identified. The state of Kentucky took over support for our genetic outreach clinics in 1987, and this has continued since. This support allows us to apply state-of-the-art technology to diagnose rare and difficult cases seen in the outreach genetic clinics as we continue to improve our clinical skills.

Dr. Carolyn Bay has been Chief of the Division of Clinical Genetics and Dysmorphology at the UK Department of Pediatrics since 2004. She actively participates in the outreach clinics and enjoys them a great deal. I am now Emeritus Professor of Pediatrics and still run the outreach clinics. Other significant people that have contributed greatly to the UK Pediatric Genetic Service are:

1. Genetic counselors Barbara Bowles Biesecker, Ron Cadle, Joyce Robl and Shannon Morrill-Cornelius;
2. Secretaries Lynda Morse and Patti McBroom-Batus;
3. Drs. Peggy Falace, C. Charlton Mabry, Jacqueline Noonan and Steve Davis;
4. All the wonderful public health nurse coordinators for each of our genetic outreach clinics.

It should be noted that prior to 1981 the UK Department of Pediatrics had a part-time genetic service run by Drs. C. Charlton Mabry and Peggy Falace via a metabolic/genetic clinic. This was supported by a March of Dimes grant. Dr. Falace eventually went into Pathology, and Dr. Mabry remains involved with his active Metabolic clinic.

During the post-1981 period, the above people have been partially responsible for the formation of the Kentucky Birth Surveillance Registry and the expansion of the Kentucky Newborn Screening Program. These two programs have placed Kentucky at the forefront of the highest-quality genetic services in the USA.

GENERAL PEDIATRICS
Academic General and Ambulatory Pediatrics

As regular pediatric residents in Philadelphia in the late 1950s, at the end of the day we would usually drift down to the residents' room in the basement where we could dictate a hospital discharge, drink a cup of coffee, recover a coat, or just sit around and grouse. Some of us were already planning to follow up in an organ-specific subspecialty fellowship. One of us, Ray Helfer, didn't want to take an organ-specific fellowship; rather, he was determined to stay in academic medicine. His military time had been in the Public Health Service at the Red Lake Indian Reservation in North Dakota, and he had seen much he could do in such a setting, as opposed to preparing to take care of middle-class children.

Ray was in the forefront of the movement to establish an academic society focused on the non-hospital care of children. Eventually, he became a full-time director of the outpatient department of Michigan State in Lansing, Mich. I remember in the early 1960s that Ray was serving as president of the Ambulatory Pediatric Association (APA). They were at the spring meetings along with the Society for Pediatric Research and the American Pediatric Society; Ray was basking in his achievement.

The APA has thrived, and its membership of more than 2,000 is made up of faculty of the divisions of General Pediatrics within the Departments of Pediatrics in all 129 medical schools. These are the special interest groups of the APA that will be meeting at the spring 2010 convention in Vancouver, B.C.:

APA SPECIAL INTEREST GROUPS

- Advocacy Training
- Child Abuse
- Community-Based Physicians
- Complex Care
- Continuity
- Culture, Ethnicity, & Health Care
- Developmental-Behavioral Pediatrics
- Division Directors in General Pediatrics
- E-Learning in Medical Education
- Emergency Medicine
- Environmental Health
- Ethics
- Evidence-Based Pediatrics
- Faculty Development
- Family Centered Care
- Fellowship Training
- Health Literacy
- Hospital Medicine
- Injury Control
- Integrative Pediatrics
- International Health
- Literacy Development Program in Primary Care
- Medical Informatics
- Medical Student Education
- Newborn Nursery
- Nutrition
- Obesity
- Pediatric Clinical Research Network
- Pediatric Emergency Medicine Program Directors
- Pediatric Residents
- Pediatric Tobacco Issues
- Pediatrics for Family Medicine
- Quality Improvement
- Race in Medicine
- School and Community Health
- Serving the Underserved
- Well-Baby Check-Ups
- Women in Medicine

What an academic general pediatrician does today is what most practicing pediatricians do, but academic pediatric faculty have the additional roles of teaching and research—in both clinical and health services—and advocacy for better health services. Most of the teaching sites for general pediatrics in pediatric departments serve poor families, usually covered for their medical insurance by Medicaid or the new Kentucky Children's Health Insurance Plan (KCHIP). These patients present more social and economic concerns in addition to their medical problems than children seen in private practice. This educational experience has been criticized by some as inadequate to prepare pediatricians for practice in the community, in which most patients are from middle-class families and have fewer social-psychological problems.

For many years, Peter Wong, M.D., headed up the General Pediatrics Division, also cross-covering for infectious disease specialists. Recently, Peter retired from full-time service. Fortunately, Dr. Bricker was able to persuade an ex-resident, Carmel Wallace of Corbin, who had been in rural private practice pediatrics for 30 years, to join the staff as chief. Additionally, he had a special interest in school problems and children with ADHD. He has encouraged our 25 general pediatrics faculty to focus on one or more of the APA interests included in the list above and to stay current in their knowledge base. They see everything, take care of most of the problems, and refer as appropriate.

Peter Wong, M.D., long-time head of General Pediatrics.

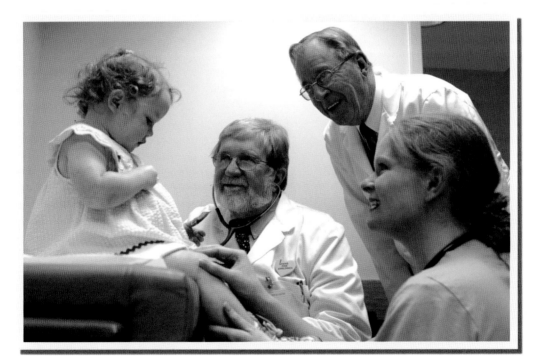

Retired private practice general pediatricians Bill Underwood (left) and Thomas Pinkstaff, who just could not quit, continued working and teaching in the General Pediatrics Clinic.

Twilight Clinic

The Twilight Clinic is a service not only for University of Kentucky regular general pediatric patients, but also to babies and children in Fayette and surrounding counties. It was conceived and has been supervised by Dr. Carol Steltenkamp since 1994. Appointments are by timely phone calls; this after-hours clinic is staffed by two or more pediatricians.

UK's Twilight Children's Clinic sees youngsters each day of the year.

Carol Steltenkamp, M.D., founder and supervisor of Twilight Children's Clinic, with two patients.

DERMATOLOGY

Instruction in dermatology at UK began before the Department of Pediatrics was created in 1960. Ullin Leavell, M.D., a dermatologist out of Duke University, in private practice since 1951 just across the street from the under-construction University Hospital, was a willing supporter of the College of Medicine. He gave 52 hours of lectures to our first class of medical students in 1960—we were short on clinical faculty. The following year, he lectured for only 26 hours. The clinical faculty were beginning to take over. Very few scored 100 on his exams, but the students were well-versed in classical dermatology.

After University Hospital began admitting patients in 1962-63, the lectures were discontinued; instead, students were assigned to day-long electives, when they accompanied Leavell on hospital consults—with residents also observing. Typically, there were two pediatric hospital consults per week, with other patients being seen in clinic. Afterward, the students followed Leavell to the animal care facility in our basement, where he was doing research. In 1965, the consult requests abruptly stopped.

This sudden halt in consult requests from Pediatrics coincided with the arrival of Dr. Doane Fischer, M.D., a pediatrician who had been in practice at the Harlan Appalachian Hospital for a decade. In his years in Harlan, Doane had developed an interest in the skin disorders of infants and children and had become self-trained in pediatric dermatology. Doane developed a slide lecture on pediatric dermatology, and every student rotation saw it. He was the expert on rashes, skin lesions, birthmarks, hair problems, and more. He was available to help diagnose and treat skin problems. He continued to consult on skin problems after he retired in 1992.

Doane died in 2008, but his dermatology expertise persists through the pediatric residents he helped train, many of them now faculty members in the Division of General Pediatrics. And Dr. Leavell, who, all these years ago, came to our rescue, has retired. In the future, we could use a well-trained pediatric dermatologist to help us with conditions such as:

Acne	Malformations of the skin
Atopic dermatitis	Melanoma
Bacterial, fungal, and viral infections	Nail dystrophy
Birthmarks	Nevi
Collagen-vascular disorders	Pigmentary abnormalities
Epidermolysis bullosa	Scabies
Genetic skin disorders	Skin rashes
Hair loss	Vascular abnormalities
Hemangiomas	Warts

END OF AN ERA

In December 1991, I went to Dr. Noonan's office for my "annual review," a once-a-year event for every Pediatrics faculty member. There was a problem, however, there was nowhere to sit. When her predecessor, Dr. Wheeler, was chairman, there were two straight chairs for visitors, and he always had a clean desk. There were a few books and journals filed in waist-high bookcases, never anything out of place. Most notable was a blue can of Prince Albert smoking tobacco and a pipe stand on the front of his desk, with several pipes ready to be picked up, tamped with Prince Albert, and lit. "OK, what do you need to talk about?"

On this occasion, however, books, reprints, working papers, and other stuff were in piles on the floor, in the bookcases, on a chair, and covering a small sofa. Noticing the problem as if for the first time, Jackie hopped up and stepped around her desk to lift a pile of journals and papers from the sofa to the floor and motioned me to sit. I then wiggled my rear into the notch created on the sofa.

She began flipping through my student evaluations and stopped. Who is this particular student who has given you this lengthy, extraordinarily high rating? I answered, "One of the students on my general pediatrics ward team." Satisfied, she moved on, later commenting, "We don't have much money, so I don't know about raises next year." We concluded by my signing her previously scored rating sheet. Then, "Chart, I have decided not to go for a fourth term as chairman. I'm stepping down." No big announcement. I guess she told everyone in this way. And, as a postscript and ironically, the student who gave me high marks is now my primary care doctor.

In the ensuing weeks, I thought a lot about Jackie—we had graduated from medical school in the same year, 1954. There were no women in my graduating class, and there were only occasional women medical students in that time period. I thought about Elizabeth Blackwell, the first woman medical graduate of an American university, about 1850. And Dr. Helen Taussig, the pediatric cardiologist at Harriet Lane Home, the children's hospital at Johns Hopkins, where she conceived of the idea of surgically correcting cardiac anomalies (Blaylock-Taussig operation for tetrology of Fallot).

Jacqueline A. Noonan, December 2008.

BREAKTHROUGHS FOR WOMEN IN AMERICAN MEDICINE

Dr. Elizabeth Blackwell was the first female medical graduate of an American university. *Souce: National Library of Medicine*

A Fluke:

Dr. Elizabeth Blackwell (1821-1910) quickly turned down by a number of medical schools finally gained admission to a small school in upstate New York, the Geneva College of Medicine. To show his liberalism, the Dean gave her application directly to the students who, thinking it was a joke, unanimously voted to admit her. Scandalized faculty and town people ostracized her during her two years of study. Students eventually accepted—even respected her. At graduation in January of 1849, ceremonies held in first Presbyterian Church of Geneva, she was not allowed to march in with other students but was acknowledged as first in her class when she climbed to the dias to receive her diploma. Later the Dean, Dr. Lee, apologized to his overseers, the faculty, and the town people, promising never again to accept a female.

Since Dr. Blackwell was not readily accepted in the medical community at large, in 1868 she established The Womens' Medical College of New York, later called The New York Dispensary for Poor Women and Children. She held the rank of Professor of Hygiene. On a subsequent mini-sabbatical to France and England she was even less accepted.

Patriotism:

At the beginning of The Civil War, Pres. Abraham Lincoln, after some persuasion, directed Secretary of War Cameron to appoint Miss Dorothea Dix female superintendent of Army nurses – a new concept for care of sick and injured soldiers. She began recruiting young ladies:

- Who are sober, earnest, self-sacrificing and self-sustained
- Who can bear the presence of suffering and exercise entire self-control of speech and manner
- Who can be calm, gentle, quiet, active, and steadfast in duty

- Over age 30
- Plain looking
- Dresses of brown or black with no bows, no curls, no jewelry, and no hoop skirts

Hundreds of these volunteers were inducted and served in the hospitals in direct care as well as menial housekeeping chores. After the war, some twenty became doctors.

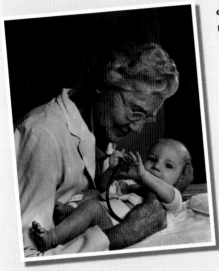

Dr. Helen Brooke Taussig conceived the idea of surgically correcting cardiac abnormalities, thereby becoming Dr. Noonan's model. *Souce: The Alan Mason Chesney Medical Archives*

Schools of Their Own:

With the doors of medical schools closed to women, women's colleges of medicine began to appear. The first in 1850, The Female Medical College of Pennsylvania/Women's Medical College of Pennsylvania, then others in Boston, New York, Baltimore, and Cleveland. Women's in Philadelphia was still in operation in 1964. All of the exclusively women's medical colleges are now closed.

Modern Acceptance:

As women in increasing numbers have begun to study in the sciences, more and more have been accepted as medical school students and entered the medical profession. Along the way, more than their share have made important contributions, two as Nobel Laureates in Medicine (Gerti Cori, 1947; Rosalyn Yalow, 1977). Of course, women now enter medical schools, are chosen for residency training, engage in clinical practice, and hold professorships in teaching institutions on equal footing with men. There were no women in my medical school class (Emory '54) and there was only one woman in our first UK medical school class ('64). With the feminist movement of the 1970s the numbers changed so that now half of our medical students are women, and pediatrics is one of the specialties they flock to.

In July 2010, the gender of our department of pediatrics faculty and housestaff is predominantely female:

	Male	Female	
Faculty	40	23	
Housestaff	19	36	**Numbers as of July, 2010**
			Source: UK Pediatrics Residency Program.

Later, in retirement, as a member of an FDA committee, Taussig is credited with the disapproval of a popular, then-new European tranquilizing drug, Thalidamide. Pregnant users were showing up with babies with congenital limb amputations. Her blowing the whistle spared our country's sharing the misery of many European families. Undoubtedly, Helen Taussig—the first woman pediatric cardiologist—was a role model for Jackie.

In 1974, the year that Jackie was appointed chairman of Pediatrics, she didn't want to be called chairwoman; 1974 was the height of the feminist movement. Jackie was never a feminist, but there had never been a woman chairman on the University campus, except in Home Economics and in the College of Nursing. The timing was good for the University, but it wasn't counting on someone who would spend 60 to 80 hours on the job each week. How lucky they were and continue to be.

Since 1974, there has been a steady increase in the number of women admitted to our medical school. Jackie has always served in some capacity on the medical school

A scientific conference was held in June 1992 at the Marriott Griffin Gate Hotel in honor of Dr. Jacqueline Noonan's retirement after her pediatric chairmanship of 18 years. Dr. Noonan, front row, center.

admissions committee, if not an official member, a Saturday-morning interviewer. Now about half of our incoming students are women, and many elect to go into pediatrics. Several have gone on to be academic pediatric cardiologists. In the spring of 1992, a two-day-long scientific tribute by current and ex-faculty and ex-residents was held for Dr. Noonan; her lifetime honors are many and various.

Dr. Noonan continues to contribute. The Endowed Chair of Pediatrics is named in her honor, and she still staffs our pediatric cardiology outreach clinics.

CHAPTER 8

Money Talks

Afurther I signed my contract in April 1961 to join the brand-new Department of Pediatrics in Lexington, I shared my good news with our across-the-street neighbors in Philadelphia. Edith, the wife, told us that she had grown up in Lexington and that her parents lived on Tates Creek Road at Albany Road. Her parents regularly had cocktail parties, so she would get us invited so that we could meet some Lexingtonians. When the invitation came a couple of weeks after we moved in, we were eager and excited.

I remember being served by a white-coated bar attendant, and we started to mingle. At that point, a dour older man in a dark suit sidled up to me and began by asking, "How are you over at the UK Hospital able to break the law—and get big salaries?" He added that "no one on the state payroll can make more money than the governor, which is $12,500 a year. I have worked at the Health Department for 10 years, and I don't make nearly that much." I couldn't respond because I was new and just did not know the local situation or how the rule got bent. My starting salary was $12,000. Since I had not earned much of anything for all the years of school and training, we were feeling wealthy.

A long-time friend of ours, a Kentuckian, told me he graduated from UK in physics, went away to Rice Institute in Houston, Texas, for his Ph.D., then returned to UK as an instructor in physics in 1959, with a starting salary of $6,500: it always lagged behind mine.

Months later, after seeing the budgets on grant and contract applications, I figured out the pediatric pay scale:

Professor .... $18,000 per annum
Associate professor 16,000
Assistant professor 14,000
Instructor 12,000

Since 1963, the instructor level has not been used because of the price war to attract talent. I had felt good about my salary because the top offer I got in Philadelphia and elsewhere was $11,500, which was good money coming from a residency that paid second-year level $50 a month and third-year level of $75 a month. But thanks to my Korean War service, we had the GI bill ($213 a month).

Recently, my wife and I had dinner with Betty Dickey, the wife of former University of Kentucky President Frank Graves Dickey (1956-1963), during whose tenure our medical school came about. She recalled that the new medical school greatly benefited their family because the UK Board of Trustees decided that the Dean of the College of Medicine should not be paid more than the University president. Overnight, Dr. Dickey's salary jumped from $12,500 a year to $20,500 a year.

This adjustment in salary for Dr. Dickey did not trickle down to faculty in other parts of the University, however, which led to a serious salary jealousy from the regular campus faculty; to some extent, it persists today. In part, this may explain why there have been so few cooperative ventures between the regular campus and the College of Medicine. But salaries of medical school faculty have always been far lower than earnings of private practitioners. And academic pediatricians are always at the bottom of the heap.

Since salary or earning equity concerns have always existed between academic physicians and private practice physicians because of the much higher earnings for those in private practice, I have always had to accept that fact. However, I was stunned when an Ashland, Ky., pediatrician, who came down for Grand Rounds on Thursday and stayed through for Saturday's football or basketball game told me he had reported his income as $75,000 a year when I had reached only $16,000. I believe that to be successful—and happy in academic pediatrics—it has to be a "calling." A review of the first Department of Pediatrics (1962) budget showed a total of $232,000 (eight faculty and staff, and office expenses).

Salaries for our faculty and staff were handled through an office in the Service Building, now the Peterson Building, with Mr. Peterson signing our checks. At first, the collections for our patient care went through the Service Building under a Physicians' Service Plan (PSP). The catch was that the University could not bill for our clinical work; rather, payments were made to individual doctors, who in turn endorsed them over to the University. There were high earners and low earners, of course.

It would seem difficult for a clinician who might spend eighty hours a week on the wards and clinics caring for patients (and then going home to study) to be treated like a campus faculty person—to be paid as if the effort were the same. And the level of responsibility! All the while, incomes for physicians in the private sector were soaring.

This disparity led to a near revolution, particularly among the "high earners." In part, I attribute this to 1) we were collecting some monies through Medicare and

Medicaid from patients who were formerly "non-pay patients," and 2) they were filling up all our appointment slots. One high-level group insurance salesman told me that so-called private patients didn't like to come to our University of Kentucky hospital or clinics because they had to sit with and mingle with "poor people." The exception was for subspecialty problems.

When our new dean, Kay Clawson, M.D., arrived in March of 1972, he was confronted with this revolt among high-earners, outlined by our then brand-new chairman, Jacqueline Noonan, as revealed during a recent interview:

> *I don't know that I had much time to think about my division of the department because so many things were happening here at UK when I became chairman. It was a very interesting time. Medicine had changed a great deal. Doctors out in the real world were making a lot of money. Doctors at the University of Kentucky College of Medicine were not making a lot of money and with all the rules of the University, although you had people who had been here by that time about 10 years, and you were limited in how much you could raise their salaries. People coming in as new faculty, in order to get anybody to come, you would have to pay them more than the people who had been here for 10 years. So the surgeons got very upset, threatening to leave the University and go into practice. I think they said they would be happy to do some teaching, but that they were about ready to walk. By that time we had a new dean, Dr. Kay Clawson, who had come as Dean. Many medical schools all over the country had developed practice plans which meant the medical school faculty became a little more independent. Instead of "full-time faculty" they became what they called "geographic full time." So, right after I became Chairman, we were in a series of discussions, all the Chairmen together discussing how we were going to manage to keep this place going with the threat of the surgeons all walking out and many people unhappy and having trouble keeping good people because of the restrictions in the University's policies. So there was going to be a practice plan with some criteria: the practice plan had to be one in which there was some incentive. People who performed better and did more work would be rewarded more than those who didn't. Each department had to have its own practice plan, and they had to be self sufficient. In other words, they had to be able to survive on their income. Everybody was worried that this would be a big problem for pediatrics. Actually, they were very worried about that—more worried about it than I was. We were being paid so little that I thought if we collected anything for what*

we got, we'd be all right. But anyhow, it took a while, but we finally got the practice plan going and one of the hardest things I really had to do was, you know the faculty had to go on either Plan A or Plan B. Plan A was that you went with the practice plan, gave up your salary, you had your tenured part of the salary, but that wouldn't have been enough to live on. But, there were a few departments that didn't want to do that and I think people had choices and I think there were some in psychiatry that stayed in the old plan at least for a while. I don't know and all the other departments signed and you had to sign a paper that really put you in the geographic rather than for full time. That was hard because I really kind of like working and not worrying about how much money I generated; as a cardiologist I was bringing in a fair amount of money for the department, so that was not the problem, but just the idea that I kind of liked having a salary, doing my job. I also recognized that this was not good for the college or for the department, you know you have to be willing to change, because change happens all the time, and we had, I think a pretty good practice plan. We had a number of people who helped develop this plan and it was one in which you know, part of this incentive was that you would have bonuses and so a bonus is what you got if the division earned more than their cost was. But we did it in such a way that even those, there are some divisions in pediatrics as there are in others that really cannot make their salary so to speak. Because they don't have any, you don't get paid by insurance companies for thinking and for making good diagnoses, you get paid for doing things to people. So, if you're not the part that does things for the division, does things to people, you're in trouble. Like infectious disease, endocrinology, very important, very important, but not people that can generate a lot of money. On the other hand, cardiology, you've got cardiac catheterizations, you've got echoes, they came around and became a money maker so to speak. And neonatology, you do a lot of procedures on babies. But we didn't have a lot of divisions that made a lot of money, but we had a couple that did pretty well, cardiology and neonatology. Now more recently of course, critical care. But we didn't have critical care as such in those days. So, we started and almost immediately everybody's salary was able to become not as high as anybody wanted, but certainly better than it had been.

Q: Did you adjust rates at that time for the various procedures that physicians would perform?

A: *I think you had, we kind of went by, you're not supposed to be able to* *find out what other people charge for things. Kentucky Medical Services Foundation (KMSF) became our billing person and I think by that time Medicaid had come in, so we were limited by our Medicaid reimbursement. Then, of course, we had insurance. But, from a department that took care of many, many patients who didn't have any insurance and no medical card, even though people complained about Medicaid, 10 dollars is better than nothing. So, we had a lot of patients with Medicaid.*

Q: Did Dr. Cunningham spearhead that effort to try to get KMSF as a billing organization in place?

A: *No, he was not involved in that. All the Chairs, Pediatrics was considered one of the major, we did have a place at the table. Actually I was the first secretary of KSMF, it's my name over there as a secretary. So, we met every week on Friday and it took a while to get started and we signed and we started doing it and pediatrics did really much better than people thought, we did all right. As time went on, and reimbursement changed, particularly for echoes, Dr. Greg Johnson was our echo person, he would sit in his office with his feet up and read echoes and make all this money while the rest of us read patients' charts, including seeing all the patients. But they kind of cut down on how much they paid for echoes, so it wasn't such a golden goose as it had been. With Neonatology, Dr. Cunningham was absolutely fantastic as far as being very careful and being sure that he followed the rules, since most of those babies did have medical cards, but he worked very closely with Medicaid. You know, Medicaid would try every way they could to find something wrong and if they came in here, he had it down, there was no question he knew what he was doing and he followed every rule to the nth degree, that's an exciting thing that happened.*

Rumors of exorbitant salaries for UK Medical Center doctors led to constant complaints by campus faculty and by people in and around Lexington. This led the *Lexington Herald-Leader* to file a request for the salaries under the Open Records Law. KMSF resisted the request for several months, claiming that it was a separate private entity from the University. In Fayette Circuit Court, it was decided that KMSF, though separate from the University for medical billing purposes, was part of the University.

So all our salary records were turned over to the newspaper, which promptly published them as headline news. The surprising thing is that the public did not react—ho hum! The reaction came from within the faculty when they saw what other faculty members were paid. This led to a lot of resentment throughout the campus and within the medical school faculty.

Over time, this resentment has subsided, and the numbers of faculty members have greatly increased because of KMSF funds. The annual statistics show that the state of Kentucky contributes directly **less than one percent** of the funds to operate the Medical Center. It is **a state-assisted** school, **not a state-supported** school. The Department of Pediatrics has grown from its original eight faculty to a current faculty of 70. Many faculty positions are now strictly service positions with no research and publication responsibilities—it is a full-service institution.

DRGs

Along with the creation of KMSF, there were outside efforts to contain and explain medical costs. In 1986, the federal government instituted Diagnostic Related Groups (DRGs), as I have mentioned—regulations aimed at hospitals and medical laboratories. Its purpose was to standardize charges and payments for the same procedures across the country. For example, hospitals would be reimbursed the same amount for treatment of a case of appendicitis, regardless of whether the costs were different with each case. Usually, the actual costs per patient varied mostly by the number of days they spent in the hospital because of complications, age, physical status, etc. This resulted in greatly shortened hospital stays and the rapid development of outpatient surgery and outpatient care in general. Today, there are several free-standing operating rooms or suites in Lexington. For example, all the ear tubes for treatment of otitis media in children are put in place in these free-standing surgeries. Incidentally, ear-tube operations have taken the place of tonsillectomies as the most frequent pediatric operation requiring general anesthesia.

During the first decade of our medical center, the Central Clinical Laboratory was the cash cow that allowed the low-earning medical school and hospital departments to exist. No charges from clinical department laboratories were allowed; this led to my laboratory's being incorporated into the Central Clinical Laboratory. In turn, this move led to an ongoing struggle for control of these monies between the chairmen of Pathology and the Medical School dean. In 1970, when Dean William Jordan summarily relieved Pathology Chairman Wellington (Pete) Stewart of his chairmanship, by the end of the month all but two of the Pathology department faculty had found positions at other medical schools. The two who stayed continued with the then newly opened Central Kentucky Blood Center on Waller Avenue, of which the University had been the main sponsor. One who left, Dr. John Koepke, eventually ended up directing the blood bank at Duke University in Durham, N.C.

I was deeply embedded in the chemistry section of the Central Clinical Laboratory, modifying all the laboratory procedures for microautomation, and I had enjoyed the whole-hearted support of Pete Stewart. Later, Dean Jordan sent an emissary to me, Earnest Chick, M.D., to ask that I continue and that I take charge of the Clinical Chemistry Section. I agreed as long as Dr. Jordan would actively search for my replacement. It turned out that my research lab and I were not relieved until four years later (1976), when Norbert Tietz, Ph.D., arrived. Dr. Tietz was already a notable clinical chemist whose textbook of clinical chemistry is now in its fourth edition. We have always enjoyed a good collegial relationship.

DRG rules have, over the years, obliterated the Central Clinical Laboratory as a cash cow for the dean or general administration. Their rates have also led to pharmaceutical companies' entering the laboratory business. Their agents now have a laboratory mailbox outside most physicians' offices, especially those in rural areas, for daily UPS or FedEx pickup, with results faxed back in one to three days. Routine lab work no longer shows the high profits for hospitals that it used to.

CPT Codes

Coupled with the inauguration of DRGs were the Current Procedural Terminology (CPT) five-digit codes. This was a system developed by the American Medical Association for standardizing the coding of physician services and procedures—a basis for health care billing. To me, it seems to allow more de-bundling of our charges to get more credit for what we do. What physicians do and the illnesses they manage are so variable that we now train and employ medical coding technicians. Several mothers of my patients are employed full time in doctors' offices and in hospitals as medical coders—another non-patient care part of the medical industry.

Children's Miracle Network

Twenty-seven years ago, singer/entertainer Marie Osmond and several friends got together to create awareness of and to raise funds for sick and injured children in local communities. Their efforts began as a small television fundraiser in Provo, Utah, and have grown to become the leading children's charity, raising more than $4 billion for 170 pediatric hospitals—The Children's Miracle Network.

Each spring in Lexington, a telethon lasting all day and evening is held to raise money for Kentucky Children's Hospital. These Kentucky funds have been used to purchase unique patient-care equipment, specially equipped ambulances, and to endow three different pediatric "chairs." These funds are magnified in that the telethon inspires other gifts throughout the year. Fund-raising has become a "business" too. Many of our "extras" for children come from these efforts. Fund development for Kentucky Children's Hospital is now year-round. Radiothons have replaced the telethon and are on several stations and in cities other than Lexington. The Makenna Foundation has funded our new pediatric emergency room. The Keeneland Concours d'Elegance supports neonatal research very generously. Dance Blue is an event by which undergraduates at UK have raised millions for pediatric cancer care. And there are many others. The Kentucky Children's Hospital Executive Development Council now raises about $2 million to $3 million per year. However much the money helps, support from the community also sends a strong and supportive message to all who labor for children.

CHAPTER 9

Internationals

I t is interesting to note that the father of American pediatrics, Abraham Jacobi (1830-1919), was a foreign medical graduate (FMG), his medical degree earned at the University of Bonn in 1851. When he traveled to Berlin to take the state medical exams, he was arrested for "high treason" because he had participated in the German Revolution of 1848, promoting political and social reforms. He had been an activist as a teenager, and for this he was imprisoned for two years. Immediately after his release, he fled Germany for New York City, arriving in 1853.

In New York City, he hung out his shingle as a practitioner of general medicine, surgery, obstetrics, and care of children. He progressively limited his practice to children, something not previously done by other doctors.

In 1860, Jacobi became Professor of Children's Diseases at the New York Medical College, holding the first "chair" in the discipline in the United States—but with no faculty. In 1865, he moved to New York University, where he introduced bedside teaching. Then from 1870 to 1902, he taught at Columbia University. Along the way, he served terms as President of the New York Medical Association and the American Medical Association.

Jacobi is best remembered, however, for his achievements in infant nutrition and his association with New York City "milk clinics." He advised parents to boil raw milk for six minutes after the first bubbles

Abraham Jacobi, M.D., the father of American pediatrics.
Photo courtesy of George Grantham Bain Collection (U.S. Library of Congress).

appeared. Pasteurization of milk did not begin in other American cities until much later—the 1930s in Lexington. Of all his contributions, boiling milk is thought to have saved more lives than any other health measure besides antibiotics. During his lifetime, every medical school in the United States established a department of pediatrics. One wonders if the determined ladies of Lexington knew of Jacobi's work and New York's milk clinics when they started the Baby Milk Supply Association in 1914.

Fast forward to 1963 when the first International appeared in our University of Kentucky Department of Pediatrics as a Resident Physician. Unlike a graduate of U.S. or Canadian medical schools, Internationals first have to pass a national board-like exam, the Foreign Medical School Graduate Record Exam, before applying for a hospital resident physician position. Perhaps only the better doctors bother to take this expensive examination. Only after passing can they participate in the annual resident matching program, or they can apply directly to a hospital with one or more residency training programs. Our match for domestic medical graduates fell short the first years of our medical school, but we were able to fill up open slots with one or more Internationals— in a way, they rescued us.

Our first Internationals were:

1962-63: Dikran Dikranian (Iran)
1963-64: Gubbi Mruthyunjaya (India)
1964-67: Joaquin Merida (Mexico)
1964-67: Insook Chung (South Korea)
1969-70: Juan Gershanik (South America)
1975-78: Ingrid Daoud (Czechoslovakia)

In our first two decades, when we had only a few beds, a small premature baby nursery, limited clinic space, and few faculty, the faculty and residents were in almost constant contact, cooperating on every baby and child. We conferred together, rounded together, ate together, picnicked together—we really knew and liked one another. Now a group like this would number more than 100. It would be possible to have a cohesive group like this only at the division level. Perhaps today, the ideal job in a medical school is to be Division Head.

The flow of Internationals into our medical center greatly increased after the end of the Vietnam War in 1975, part of a nation-wide surge. Some of the enticement for them to come was that after their resident training program, they could stay in the United States if they practiced in a medically underserved area. In Kentucky, that meant rural or mountainous Kentucky. But many have somehow found ways to stay at our Lexington and Louisville medical schools in highly specialized positions.

This influx of foreign doctors has helped Kentucky meet some critical health-care needs. As a state, we are still under-doctored. As of April 2009, 9655 doctors reported a practice address in Kentucky. This total does not include 630 retired physicians. The current tabulation is:

Medical school attended	Number	Percent of total
In Kentucky	4,009	41.5
Elsewhere in U.S.	3,643	37.7
International	2,003	20.8
	9,655	100.0

Not surprisingly, at the current time, one in every five doctors in Kentucky is international; we could not get along without out international colleagues. But how long can their native countries tolerate the "brain drain?" On the other hand, many of the international pediatricians (especially those in academics) have more profoundly improved the care of children in their countries of origin as visitors than they could have possibly done by practicing there.

The International clinician who stands out as a model of what a doctor could be is Nirmala (Nima) Desai. Nima joined us in 1973 during the transition of Dr. Beargie's Special Nursery to the NICU of Dr. Cunningham. Nima was the bridge for those babies; she came to Lexington, unannounced, with her urologist husband, who was establishing a private practice. She had only partially completed a training program in the developing subspecialty of neonatology at Boston Children's Hospital.

Nima has taught, has interacted with, and has been a role model for every pediatric resident since 1973, all the while maintaining her cultural identification, wearing a sari every day for work and social events and also keeping her Indian accent. There is no doubt that she is from India, yet she interacts with all Kentuckians in a way they understand. In addition to her duties in the NICU, she maintains the Special Well-Baby Clinic to follow those preemies until they have caught up.

Nirmala Desai, M.D.
Maharaja Sayayiro
University, Baroda, India;
1973-present

It should be noted that some international pediatricians continued their training beyond the three years of pediatric residency to become subspecialists, preparing themselves to deliver the "advanced care" now required at a University medical center. Some of these Internationals who head up UK pediatric divisions are:

Peter Wong, General Pediatrics, Infectious Diseases (Thailand)

Jamshed Kanga, Pulmonary (Pakistan)

Henrietta Bada, Neonatology (Philippines)

Horacio Zaglul, Critical Care (South America)

Stefan Kiessling, Nephrology (Germany)

H.R. Shashidhar, Gastroenterology (India)

Throughout the Pediatric Department's divisions there are others who are caring for children and doing applied research. It is clear that international doctors fill many essential slots.

The culmination of contributions from international physicians in 1992 to our department is Vipul Mankad, then vice chairman of Pediatrics at the University of South Alabama-Mobile, who responded to our search for a new chairman of Pediatrics. Mankad was a pediatric hematologist who had made his mark studying sickle cell anemia, a major health issue in Alabama. His studies had been well funded by the National Institutes of Health. Dr. Mankad was interviewed by only a few members of the department, so we were actually surprised when Dean Emery Wilson announced Dr. Mankad's appointment.

Vipul N. Mankad, M.D.
Maharaja Sayayiro University
Baroda, India
Chairman: 1992-2003
In 1997, Dr. Mankad cut the ribbon signifying the opening and dedication of the new Children's Hospital within a hospital.

There were a number of members, largely junior, of the department who were pulling for an internal candidate who was popular with the students; while older members of the department were hoping for a new chief who had an established reputation outside his or her own school—had published meaningful research and was a member of the by-invitation-only pediatric societies. Dean Wilson recognized the turmoil and called a meeting with the tenured faculty to explain his choice—most importantly, that Dr. Mankad had arrived with a plan for a Children's Hospital. In time, the internal candidate left. However, Dr. Mankad became aware of this division in the department as soon as he arrived in September 1992.

Since I had not interviewed Dr. Mankad prior to his appointment, as an old professor with not much time left, I didn't even know what he looked like. In May 1992, when he was elected to the American Pediatric Society, a milestone in a successful pediatric professor's career, I went to our meeting in hopes of introducing myself and welcoming him to Kentucky. He did not attend, however, and was elected *in absentia*. It was difficult for me to understand how someone would miss this honor bestowed by his peers.

When Dr. Mankad arrived in September 1992, he called us together and delivered a practiced speech, a speech that emphasized what he stood for professionally; he wanted our department to move forward, and he understood that it took money—which was promised by the administration—including the creation of a Children's Hospital. He was focused and had hit the ground running with plans in his hands. I became his advocate.

Over the next several months he would flash by the open door of my office and never look sideways. Finally, I introduced myself when we were standing together at the fourth-floor clinic elevator. After a slow start, our relationship became cordial, but not close, and he made a memorable event out of my first retirement in 1995. A long relationship developed when he couldn't find anyone to take my job. I stayed on part-time, still see patients, and head up our division.

In May 1993, when I was at the San Diego airport returning from a pediatric meeting, I found Mankad waiting for the same plane. We sat together for a while; then he got busy on his laptop, writing memos and playing with numbers. Eventually, our flight was called, and he and I boarded and began working our way to our seats. To my surprise, sitting just behind first class, was my first mentor, Waldo E. Nelson. Nelson, then 91 years old, long widowed, and now under the supervision of his two daughters, apparently had been pre-boarded. I doubled back for a brief visit, then told Mankad that that man was Waldo Nelson! I couldn't believe the puzzled expression on Mankad's face. After all, Dr. Nelson's *Textbook of Pediatrics* has been the world-wide authority on Pediatrics since the 1950s. Currently, it is in its 18th edition in 27 languages. At this moment, I realized that Dr. Mankad was not "into famous people."

Over a few years, Dr. Mankad recruited numerous general pediatricians and some subspecialists, doubling the number of pediatric faculty from 27 to 54—quite an achievement. He, along with Dr. Steltenkamp, started the Twilight Clinic, an evening children's clinic that has greatly reduced emergency clinic visits. The Problem Based Learning method, advocated by David Wilson, was allowed to die. It had been designed for use where there is a dearth of patients; in Kentucky there have always been enough sick children. In its place, we returned to the traditional methods of bedside, lecture, and conference teaching. The highlight of Mankad's tenure as department head came when the Children's Hospital was completed in August 1997, and with its integration into the over-all medical center.

By 1997, things began to slow down, along with the shrinking budget across the whole medical center, and faculty began slipping away at an alarming rate. During my annual review in December 2001, Dr. Mankad told me that he was going to resign soon. Later, my wife and I were among the five pediatric couples invited to his farewell event at a large new hotel. Most of the guests were department heads and ranking administrators throughout the College of Medicine and the University.

From UK, Dr. Mankad embarked on a new career involving policy, money, and development. Directly from UK, he went to Washington as a Robert Wood Johnson Foundation Fellow, as an advisor to the U.S. Senate Committee on Health. From there he became the Chief Medical Officer at Children's Hospital and Research Center in Oakland, Calif. Most recently, he has become the CEO of Qualités, a private company that helps clients with institutional development.

While at Kentucky, Vipul's personal style did not make everyone like or love him, but, to his credit, he moved the Department of Pediatrics significantly forward during his eleven years. He was the man for the moment.

A youngster is fitted with a bike helmet at a health fair held on UK's campus on Aug. 23, 1997, to coincide with the ribbon cutting to open the Kentucky Children's Hospital. *Photo courtesy Lexington Herald-Leader.*

CHAPTER 10

Critical Care

Pediatric Critical Care, as we now know it, became institutionalized in 1987, when the first certifying examination was offered. Fellowship training programs had begun in the 1970s, until now there are 59 approved three-year programs. Pediatric intensivists have greatly increased the survival rate of critically ill children. There are pediatric ICUs in all children's hospitals, and every hospital for adults has an ICU.

When you take the long view, critical care has been practiced for many, many years. I remember in the 1930s at St. Mary's Hospital in Knoxville, Tenn., there was a requirement that you had to hire a "private duty nurse" to assist in your care if you or your patient would require constant round-the-clock care. "Regular" nurses just didn't have time. There was a list of private duty nurses on call, the beginning of Nurse Registries. There was no health insurance at the time, so you paid "out-of-pocket."

When I was five years old, I came down with summertime gastroenteritis, diarrhea, and dehydration. Dr. Brown came to the house, and immediately packed me off to St. Mary's. I did not get any intravenous fluids, only oral rehydration, as now practiced in third-world countries. There was no intravenous equipment or special supplies for children. After a week of drinking fluids in the hospital, I was judged well enough to go home. When I came home, my parents' bedroom was cleared out and the bed covered with only white sheets, for it was a hot summer. I was fed clear soup and Jell-O for days. I don't know where my parents slept, but I remember Dr. Brown's stopping by every day. I wonder if I had had a short course of intravenous fluids in the ER if this lengthy illness would have been shortened to only one or two days.

Fast forward to 1952, when I was a third-year medical student in training at Atlanta's Grady Memorial Hospital. Intravenous fluid therapy was being used on the wards, but it came in reusable, autoclaved glass bottles with reused rubber hoses and a #20 gauge needle (a standard syringe needle) with the end of the hose stretched over the hub of the needle. Infants and small children were spared the IV needle, however, by using a long spinal-tap needle for electrolyte fluid administered subcutaneously, 20 to 40 ml scapula to pelvis, leaving a long sausage-like hump down both sides of their backs. These big ridges of electrolyte fluid would be slowly absorbed over the next one or two hours, but certainly not the controlled intravenous pump infusions we use today.

After my three-year stint in the U.S. Navy during the Korean War, I began my pediatric residency at St. Christopher's Hospital in Philadelphia. Intravenous therapy was much improved from Grady Hospital, but we were fabricating our own plastic tubing and cut-off needles sharpened on a whetstone. However, we were purchasing fluids pre-prepared in bottles from Baxter, Inc. Pyrogen reactions were no longer a problem, and long, narrow-gauge plastic tubing was much easier to use. At night, the open wards looked like an IV jungle. When my wife and I visited hospitals in Western China in 1984, we recognized the red rubber tubing and glass bottles.

Fluid and electrolyte therapy became a province of pediatricians since babies and children are more vulnerable to imbalances because the proportion of fluids in their bodies is greater than that of adults, and the turnover is faster. Moreover, the measure of a pediatric resident became how quickly and how efficiently he could start and maintain an IV. When my rotation called for assignment in the nursery, I was stationed in Temple University Hospital. On several occasions, I was called away from the nursery to start a difficult IV on some elderly patient with "rolley" veins—a bit of status among the other residents.

When I came to Kentucky in 1961, I was glad to find that commercially manufactured IV needles already on thin tubing (butterflies) had just been introduced. Because they cost more than the homemade ones, they were rationed. They had ultra-sharp thin-wall needles and were so much easier to use on our small patients.

From the outset, our house officers were responsible for diagnostic blood drawing, but this changed in 1970 for efficiency of lab operations. We were using roller-pump automated chemistries by then, and performing the tests worked out best when all the specimens were loaded before the train of equipment was started. If we were able to start 90 percent of the day's work in the laboratory before 9 a.m., we could handle the few remaining tests throughout the day with ease. After some 10 to 20 years, robot chemistries replaced roller-pump automated chemistries, largely because we were not tied to running batches.

To facilitate this arrangement, phlebotomists were hired and trained to collect specimens throughout the day, with one always at beck and call on the hospital floors. In the process, our house officers' hand skills rapidly declined, as did their ability to do other procedures (e.g. lumbar taps). Also, the babies and their veins got smaller and smaller. As an indication of this loss of hand skills, Dr. Heinrich Werner, head of Pediatric

Intensive Care (PICU), began performing all the elective lumbar taps by appointment in the 1990s because he was good at it. The hand skills of all the intensivist doctors were the best ones for phlebotomies; they were also performing femoral punctures, jugular phlebotomies, scalp vein phlebotomies, and other body taps and aspirations. At the September 2009 Children's Miracle Network fund-raiser, money was sought to purchase a $4,300 ultrasound vein identifier to make venipunctures easier to perform. Imagine finding a viable vein on a one-pound preemie.

In 1980, the previous quarters of the Premature/Sick Baby Nursery on the east side of the main hallway across from the central nursing station was declared the PICU, with Drs. Cottrill, Broughton, and Noonan as attending physicians. Hospital administration gave only half-hearted support for this move, so other sources were tapped. The Lexington Junior League donated eight monitors, and other equipment came through the Children's Miracle Network, repeated over the years. Even so, the unit was understaffed. That crisis came when a cardio-thoracic surgeon, Ed Todd, refused to perform open-heart surgery on a child unless he could have one-on-one

Heinrich Werner, M.D., vice chairman and associate professor of UK's Department of Pediatrics, was also medical director of the Kentucky Children's Hospital Division of Pediatric Critical Care when he died of cancer in July 2007 at age 49. He also served as interim chairman of the Department of Pediatrics in 2003-2004. He received his medical degree from the University of Mainz Medical School in West Germany.

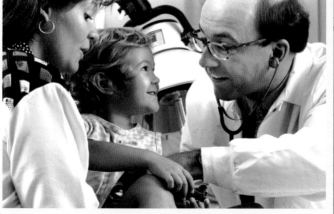

Heinrich Werner came to UK directly from his Pediatric Critical Care Fellowship in 1994 and helped build the Pediatric Intensive Care Unit here. He also established the pediatric sedation service, which is staffed by five intensivists.

round-the-clock nursing for that child. Private-duty nursing as in olden days? In time, hospital administration capitulated.

By this time, the feeling surfaced that hospital administration would never acknowledge or fulfill the needs of a fully modern Pediatrics Department. Not only did the new PICU care for post-surgical patients, but also for most pediatric medical patients such as those with Reye's syndrome, metabolic acidosis of various inborn errors of metabolism, life-threatening pulmonary disorders, trauma cases such as shaken-baby syndrome, for Guillain-Barre syndrome, Down syndrome, babies with congenital heart disease in heart failure, and on and on.

We used to have, on average, two children with diabetic ketoacidosis on the fourth floor continuously. At presentation to our Emergency Room, they typically were semistuporous or in coma. I would cancel my planned day and stay at or near bedside for the day, guiding fluid, electrolyte, and insulin replacement so as to avoid cerebral edema and other complications. I was pleasantly surprised when these children started being admitted to the PICU and closely monitored according to protocol. As long as I touched base throughout the first day, I could have a life elsewhere. I would see these children in clinic for years to come.

In 1973, Dr. Noonan had designated a large room on 4 West as an intensive care site, and asked Dr. Carol Cottrill to supervise the new unit. There were four beds or bassinets, one in each corner, with the nurse's desk in the center close to the windows. It was staffed by two nurses on each shift. The signature case that prompted Noonan's decision was a baby, Dakota, with a post-surgical short gut syndrome. She required constant feeding and attention. The room was always full, and the pressure for more intensive care beds kept mounting.

Parallel with starting our small intensive care unit, new high-tech equipment such as small respirators, heart monitors, cardio ECHO monitors, IV pumps, mechanical beds, etc., were coming on the market and were enhancing the care of desperately ill babies and children. This led to larger quarters with in-wall O_2, air, and electrical outlets. We were not copying other hospitals, rather making practical adjustments to patient care needs on our own pediatric floor.

While our beginning PICU was in the area now used as pediatric resident quarters, there was no permanent equipment. As I have related, with the help of Lexington's Junior League and the Children's Miracle Network, Dr. Cottrill obtained necessary medical equipment, some of which is still being used today—Hewlett-Packard modular monitors that allow for monitoring blood pressure, pulse rate, EKG, breathing, intracranial pressure, etc. Other equipment for PICU was obtained by means of gifts from various agencies and benefactors. The PICU then occupied what is now Pharmacy quarters, Room 411.

In 1992, when Vipul Mankad became the chairman of the Department of Pediatrics, he wanted all the division heads to be sub-board certified, but Dr. Cottrill was not sub-board certified in critical care. Mankad seemed to be looking at framed wall certificates and not at a doctor's proven experience and capabilities. So when a downtown financial officer from Durham, N.C., was transferred to Lexington, he let it be known that he wanted his critical care-specialist wife to be hired by our Medical Center. Subsequently, in 1993, Jana Stockwell became the head of the Critical Care Division; she hired two additional staff. Dr. Cottrill learned that she was no longer a critical care attending physician (no longer on the schedule) only at a department meeting. It happened that financier Stockwell, along with his wife, Jana, moved on to Atlanta after one year. Dr. Cottrill felt that she had been terribly disrespected, so she left UK and opened a private practice of pediatric cardiology at Central Baptist Hospital, where she was very successful. Several years ago, our Department of Pediatrics bought her practice; that particular money she gave to the University of Kentucky College of Arts and Sciences. There is now a healthy working relationship between Dr. Cottrill and our department. She is one of us once again, as she should be—to our great advantage.

After Dr. Stockwell left, she was replaced by a pediatric critical care trainee who was behind her in the Duke University fellowship program. Heinrich Werner, M.D., was a high-quality person and a strong contributing faculty member. He was from Germany, but had come to the United States for general pediatrics training and a fellowship in pediatric critical care. He became very adept with his hand skills and was the designated doctor to perform lumbar taps, especially to obtain diagnostic cerebral spinal fluid on non-emergent cases. Heinrich also served as interim chairman of the Department of Pediatrics from 1993-94, guiding us through some troublesome times. He was appointed temporary department chair when Dr. Mankad left with very short notice.

Heinrich became vice-chair and Children's Hospital medical director with the new department chairman, J. Timothy Bricker, M.D., bringing forward a department with a balanced budget and general good will in 2004. In 2007, however, Heinrich developed a rapidly growing oral sarcoma resistant to therapy. He died in 2008, which saddened us terribly. The unit was renamed The Heinrich Werner, M.D., Pediatric Critical Care Unit, now located in our recently autonomous Kentucky Children's Hospital.

Heinrich's death left a deep sense of loss in all. Typical among the eulogies:

> *"Dr. Werner was a consummate physician," said Dr. Jeffrey Moscow,*
> *Professor, Department of Pediatrics, UK College of Medicine, and Chief*
> *of Pediatric Hematology/Oncology. "We appreciated so much his medical*
> *knowledge and his clinical judgment. He was the calm in the eye of the*
> *storm. He was a leader, teacher, and role model to medical students,*

resident physicians, and faculty alike. For us his death is a tremendous loss."

Dr. Joe Iocono, Assistant Professor, Departments of Pediatrics and Surgery, UK College of Medicine, and a pediatric surgeon, said, "Heinrich embodied the very core of who all of us strive to be—a gifted clinician; a devoted husband and father; a mentor for students, residents, and fellow faculty; and above all, a champion for children's health care in our region. I have lost a friend and a mentor, and I will miss him dearly."

Dr. Werner was succeeded by Dr. Cheri Landers, who trained at Texas Children's Hospital in Houston. After adopting a baby and wanting to be at home more, she went part time. She has taken a leading role in our new quality improvement program. Dr. Horacio Zaglul, a native of Argentina but English- and American-trained, is now leading the division. They now describe themselves as pediatric subspecialists, providing comprehensive care for the critically ill or injured infants, children, or adolescents. Their services include the use of mechanical ventilation, extracorporeal life support, dialysis, and hemofiltration, as well as invasive and non-invasive cardio-respiratory monitoring. This unit and these doctors are always extremely busy.

Enabling many of the improvements in Critical Care Medicine has been the miniaturization of equipment and the development of robot chemistry, which allows for a full array of tests, using fewer than 100 microliters of plasma or serum, available on a moment's notice. An overall effort to save every baby, infant, and child has prompted a concern about the costs of providing critical care to very tiny babies (less than 1 ½ pounds) and consideration of the ethics of providing costly care to children with limited chances of survival or meaningful recovery. For the moment, we will leave that to the ethicists—all our patients will continue to get the old college try.

CHAPTER 11

Access

John F. Kennedy's first exposure to Appalachia came during the presidential campaign of 1960, when Hubert Humphrey, a well-liked politician by West Virginians, accompanied Kennedy throughout West Virginia. Kennedy had never seen the poverty of the coal fields before, and it made a lasting mark on him. West Virginia went blue. After the election, the Kennedy administration began sending scouts into the region to gather information.

Dr. Doane Fischer, then the pediatrician at the Harlan Miners' Hospital, was host to Bobby Kennedy as he walked through and discussed their hospital. This was one stop on Kennedy's tour, and other Washington agents followed. Movement on doing something helpful to Appalachia was afoot. Then came the assassination on Nov. 22, 1963.

Pres. Lyndon Johnson took the baton, and his initial foray into Appalachia is described below.

Stimulus Package—1964

With great media coverage, Pres. Lyndon B. Johnson (LBJ) visited a typical unemployed Eastern Kentucky man and his family in Beauty (Martin County) on Friday, April 24, 1964. The tar-paper shack was near the helicopter landing strip where he and his wife, Lady Bird, had landed. They were a little late because 1,500 people came to greet him, and he attempted to shake hands with them all.

At the house perched on a high bare bank, LBJ and Tom Fletcher had a 10-minute earnest discussion, sitting and squatting on the porch. Fletcher told LBJ that he had been out of work for almost two years and had learned only $400 in 1963, $400 that came from work at a sawmill and selling coal he picked up at an abandoned mine.

Fletcher, 38, had eight children; his oldest, an 18-year-old son, and

17-year-old daughter had dropped out of school in the fourth grade. Finally, as LBJ arose, he shook hands and said, "Be seeing you—goodbye." Then he paused and walked back to Fletcher. "What I want you to do for me is to keep those kids in school. I mean the girls, too, not just the boys." Lady Bird departed with a wave and called, "Bye chillun."

Later that day, the county judge told LBJ that most residents who have jobs work in nearby West Virginia or not-too-far-away Ohio. In this Kentucky county of 14,000 people, 37 percent were jobless. The judge told the president that his county had no newspaper, no radio station, and no hospital, and that once a week a doctor comes from Prestonsburg.

The Man on Horseback

Louisville Courier-Journal on April 25, 1964, political cartoon of Pres. Lyndon B. Johnson riding to the rescue of an Appalachain waif. *Courtesy © The Courier-Journal.*

LBJ and his small entourage went on to two other locations in Kentucky and met with Appalachian politicians in West Virginia, North Carolina, and South Carolina. After his 17-day tour of Appalachia, LBJ took his "war on poverty" to Pittsburgh, the largest Appalachian city. He told steel workers and hill-country sawmill workers: "I wish I could look into every face and shake every hand." You might have thought he already had—his right hand was puffed and daubed with red antiseptic.

Information from Lexington Herald, Lexington, Ky., Saturday morning April 25, 1964, and Lexington Leader, Lexington, Ky., Saturday evening, April 25, 1964.

From this tour and LBJ's efforts came the Appalachian Regional Commission (ARC), which continues to funnel federal money into the region. For the most part, ARC funds have been used for road improvements. In Kentucky, gravel roads have been blacktopped, hundreds of small bridges built or replaced, U.S. 23 into southeastern Kentucky four-laned, and plans initiated for another interstate highway (I-66) made to run from Pikeville to London and across Kentucky, east to west. Purchase of right-of-way continues to this day.

Before and After ARC Roadways in Kentucky

One of ARC's early funding projects was what was commonly called the "Happy Pappy Program" for unemployed fathers. It was most visible when gangs of men went along cleaning up the sides of Eastern Kentucky roads with their sickles, rakes, and black plastic bags. They didn't move with much alacrity and smoked tons of cigarettes.

The net effect of ARC's activity was to make the population more mobile, and it became increasingly easier to get to University Hospital. This led to the fast-developing clinical overload that began in the late 1960s. In turn, heretofore triple-threat doctors (research-clinical-teaching) pulled out of labs toward all-clinical service. I haven't had or sponsored an NIH-laboratory grant for 40 years—my publications becoming all clinical. Our research laboratories are now mostly staffed by Ph.Ds. We could become like small medical schools that make little or no effort at research. But we have much to offer—the pendulum is beginning to swing back the other way.

Getting There

In June of 1965, the Pediatrics Department got a telephone call from Mrs. Tommy Duncan, the medical coordinator for Wayne County Head Start. Wayne County, at the time, was 200 miles south on the Tennessee-Kentucky state line. The road the entire way was a two-lane macadam road, and Monticello, the county seat, was at least four hours from Lexington. One of Head Start's goals was to do a health assessment, which included a physical exam by a doctor. She already had asked the two local doctors,

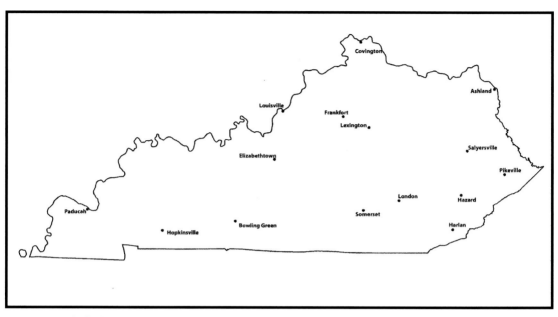

1960: Kentucky had NO 4-lane interstate highways or parkways. All U.S. highways in the state were two lanes, some with shoulders and some without.

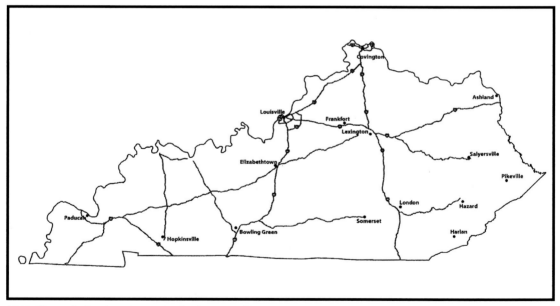

2010: Kentucky's 4-lane interstate highways and parkways.

but they were too busy to leave their offices. I agreed to come down and examine her children, who were located in two elementary schools. When I arrived late morning at her husband's pharmacy, she was eager to show me around and to get started. She especially wanted me to examine two young boys, Amos and Roger. "They can't open their mouths, we can hardly get a teaspoon into their mouths."

She was correct, and I also found that they couldn't open their hands unless they were fully volar flexed—their fingers closed up when they extended and dorsi-flexed their hands. At the end of the day, when all the children had been packed into their school buses and had sped away, Mrs. Duncan volunteered to take me out to Amos' and Roger's home on Sunnybrook Road, leading to the Tennessee Picket State Park.

We got out of her car, slammed the doors, and kicked the tires so we wouldn't be sneaking up or surprising them. As we walked up the path, the mother, who had been at the school, started yelling, "Obie, hit's the doctor, Obie, hit's the doctor." Old Obie looked up from cranking his corn sheller and began clearing the porch, kicking sleeping hound dogs—dogs were scrambling in all directions trying to get out of the way of his boot.

I had a nice long conversation with both parents, and they showed me how wide they could open their mouths, hands, and fingers. Obie could barely open his. As we sat together on the porch, we talked and I had some questions. When I got home to Lexington near midnight, I debriefed for my wife. She later wrote the following poem:

PERSPECTIVE

After his wife shouted
    that company is here,
Old Obie did his part:
    He cleared the front porch,
by kicking each hound dog off
    with well-placed dusty boots.
Now the old man sits relaxed
    in his rump-sprung chair
rocking and chewing.
    Occasionally he spits.

    We talk, he rocks.
Have you traveled much? I ask.
    Oh, some, he says. 'Nuff.
Ever get out of the county?
    Yessir.
Out of the state?
    Nawsir. Never wanted to.
Not even to see what goes on
in other places? I persist.

Nawsir.
Ever been to Lexington, then?
Once't, he says.
And ... how did you like that?
Well, he says, rocking, chewing –
speculative, then certain,
he spits, then says:
Hit won't 'mount to nothin' –
Hit's too fur away.

Barbara Mabry

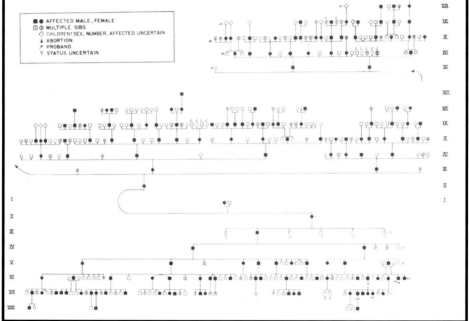

Synoptic pedigree showing eight generations of a family from Wayne County, Ky., afflicted with Trismus pseudocamptodactyly syndrome, or Dutch-Kentucky syndrome. This disorder was later shown to be a variant of Carney complex, a familial cardiac myxoma condition and complications.

REFERENCES

Mabry CC, Barnett, IS, Sorenson, HW: Trismus pseudocamptodactyly syndrome, J. Pediatrics 85: 503-508, 1974.

Yeugelers M, Bressan M, McDermontt DA, Weremowicz, S, Morton CC, Mabry CC, Lefaivre J-F, Zunaman A, Chaudron J-M, Basson CT: Mutation of perinatal myosin heavy chain associated with a Carney complex variant and trismus-pseudocamptodactyly syndrome, N Eng J Med 351:460-469, 2004.

Old Obie was right in that it was difficult to get back and forth to Lexington from Sunnybrook Road in Wayne County, but four-lane highways were just beginning to punch their way into Kentucky—none, however, into Kentucky's Appalachia. Certainly there were no four-lane highways, interstates, or parkways in Kentucky as the UK College of Medicine began in 1960. And before 1960, a lot of travel in and out of Appalachia was made in day-cars attached to coal or log trains. The railroads were more developed than the roads. I once rode the C&O Railroad overnight from Lexington to Washington, D.C. As I was fumbling through my pocketbook while getting off, I asked the porter, "How much is your usual tip?" He said, "Five dollars, but I rarely gets it."

An old doctor who began practice in Breathitt County in 1920 once told me that there were no roads there, but you could get in or out by riding the passenger car attached right behind the coal-car connected to the coal-fired steam engine of a coal train almost every day. More recently, an old friend, now retired to Jackson County, was helping his wife write the history of the county where he grew up. Old timers told him that, until U.S. 421 was built after World War II, "you rode the passenger car attached to a log train to East Bernstadt (Ky.), then you could go anywhere in the world." East Bernstadt is on the North/South-running U.S. 25, with the Southern Railroad parallel.

In 1960, there was no organized Emergency Medical Ambulance and Technician (EMT) service or system. If you drove south on U.S. 25 toward Corbin, there might be a fund-raising traffic stop at each county seat to raise money for an ambulance. Even in Lexington, the ambulances were owned by the funeral homes, and if you were in an accident, a hearse was likely to scoop you up and head to one of our hospital emergency rooms—just a driver—no trained medical assistant. In 1962, unconscious after a horrible automobile accident, I was loaded along with my wife and four children into the back of an ambulance. The driver and his helper rode up front and smoked. We had waited over an hour to be picked up.

Beginning in the late 1960s, our University Hospital set up an Emergency Room Service that doubled as an EMT training post. Later, the city got into the ambulance service business as we know it today. However, we still needed a special transport system for babies, particularly prematurely born babies born in remote parts of the state.

When the first 40-mile leg of the Bert T. Combs Mountain Parkway from Winchester to

Paul Maddox, M.D. and Bertie Centers, R.N.

One of the first ambulances to come to the UK Emergency Room via the Mountain Parkway in the 1960s.

Campton in Wolfe County was built and dedicated in October 1962, it created a toboggan-slide run from the Kentucky River drainage area right into Lexington and the University Hospital. One cannot drive up the first leg of the Mountain Parkway today without seeing one or more ambulances in the oncoming lanes, headed for Lexington.

This clear-run to Lexington introduced us to Dr. Paul Maddox, who was written up in 1962 as the busiest doctor in the country by the national magazine, *Medical Economics*. Typically, he referred a patient with only a cryptic prescription-pad note, but we usually treated his patients as "direct admits"—having learned that they were always seriously ill or hurt. Dr. Maddox built his office in campton, including a small operating room/delivery room, onto the side of his house, so he was available 24 hours a day. Maddox once told me that the greatest help University Hospital gave him was somewhere to send sick or prematurely born babies. Before we opened, all he could do with a preemie was to wrap it in aluminum foil, feed it, keep it warm, and hope for its survival.

In the 1970s, money from the Children's Miracle Network telethon paid for a special neonatal transport ambulance to go and pick up a prematurely born or distressed newborn up to 80 miles away. And in

Exterior of the first neonatal transport ambulance at UK Hospital, 1974.

Interior of the first neonatal transport ambulance.

Helicopter service began to transport patients to both the Intensive Care Unit (ICU) and to the Neonatal Intensive Care Unit (NICU) in 1979.

1979, helicopter service to bring patients to both our Intensive Care Unit (ICU) and to our Neonatal Intensive Care Unit (NICU) was initiated. At first, the National Guard based in Frankfort would pick up our transport team at the heliport on the south side of where Commonwealth Stadium now stands and fly to distant hospitals in Eastern Kentucky to pick up a prematurely born baby or a sick or injured child and bring them back to the helipad, where an ambulance shuttled them to University Hospital Pediatric ICU or NICU. For the first two or three years, a resident doctor and several nurses would go on the trips.

In a story that came to me at this time, a community hospital in Corbin called for a helicopter transport of a prematurely born infant to our newly opened NICU. The baby's doctor and nurses followed instructions and had the baby in an isolette waiting at the door to the back parking lot of the hospital. As it was told, all is in readiness, and here comes the helicopter, right on schedule. As it is about to touch down, a snowstorm of paper and garbage so thick you couldn't see occurs—the lids on all the dumpsters were open!

When the propeller blades of the copter stopped, all the paper and debris drifted to the ground and to the tops of everything else. The nursery team rushed the baby to the waiting, door-open copter. As it lifted off, the snowstorm recurred. Later that day, the doctor took his car to the car wash; it immediately became hospital policy to keep the lids closed on the dumpsters at all times.

Eventually, a commercial helicopter service company got the franchise and stationed one helicopter atop University Hospital and one in an Eastern Kentucky location. Staffed by specially trained EMTs and nurses, they could move a patient from a distant location (such as Pikeville or Harlan) in about 30 minutes.

In 2005, a larger national helicopter service began to provide our transport, with a larger area of coverage. Most of the medical team, which flies and receives, is based at University Hospital, with Dr. Philip Bernard of our Pediatric ICU in charge. Last year, there were more than 700 pediatric transports to University Hospital.

I think that one of my patients, Michael, holds the record for the most transports for a single patient. He was air-lifted from the Harlan ARH 25 times in his first two years of life for unexplained severe metabolic acidosis. Finally, we diagnosed him with the super-rare congenital-hereditary disorder—B-ketothiolase deficiency, recently redesignated 3-Oxothiolase (mitochondrial acetoacyl-CoA lyase) deficiency. He and his mother have moved to Lexington, where he is in high school. He attends Metabolic Clinic regularly.

Getting here can still be a major problem. Recently, I had a patient from Phelps, on the most Eastern tip of Kentucky, now a 3 ½-4 hour ride to Lexington. Only the grandmother in the family has a car, so Mamaw volunteered to drive seven-year-old Hollie Beth and her mother to Lexington. As the day for the appointment neared, Mamaw panicked at having to drive so far, plus cope with Lexington traffic. Her truck-driver son came to the rescue with his truck's GPS. He programmed the GPS for UK Medical Center, and she was good to go. She, her daughter, and Hollie Beth finally showed up in clinic. They got to Lexington on time, but GPS instructions took them straight to our hospital loading dock. She was more than an hour late to clinic.

PAYING FOR IT

During the early 1960s, Lewis "Bud" Cochran, Ph.D., provost for the University, was tracking Medical Center expenses, particularly hospital expenditures. He would regularly buttonhole me between Sunday School and church service to complain that we were spending too much money over at the Medical Center—and bleeding the University dry! For the most part, this was because our patients were poor and uninsured. Private-paying patients were not selecting our hospital; rather, their private doctors were continuing to admit them to the three private hospitals in Lexington and community hospitals in outlying areas. Since Dr. Willard's early

Philip Bernard, M.D., consults with physician liaison Tarra Crane. Dr. Bernard, an ICU doctor, is the medical director of Pediatric Transport and Outreach. He and registered nurse Shelly Marino head up the transportation systems for ferrying pediatric patients to the University of Kentucky.

concept was that University Hospital would be a referral hospital, exemplary care could be provided and demonstrated. We would be the gold standard. He could not then have understood the needs and psyche of the region as they were then and as they have evolved over the years.

In 1970, when Peter Bosomworth was appointed Chancellor of the Medical Center in place of the departed Dr. Willard, he kept dropping the statement, "We need to improve patient access to care." I thought at the time that he was referring to making it easier for patients to get to Lexington over Kentucky's gravel and two-lane macadam roads. They were already getting to our doors; however, he was talking about their having insurance or some means to pay their bills. The hospital was struggling on start-up monies that were not increasing, yet the patient load was getting heavier.

Pediatrics did its part in this financial-stress period by holding general pediatric and pediatric cardiology clinics deep into Eastern Kentucky and bringing only the sickest children back to University Hospital. At the same time, Pres. Lyndon Johnson was pushing federal legislation for Medicare for the elderly and Medicaid for the indigent. In the spring and summer of 1965, he maneuvered both Medicare and Medicaid through the U.S. House of Representatives (April 7, 1965) and the U.S. Senate (July 9, 1965). President Johnson delayed signing the bills, however, until he could get to Independence, Mo. On July 30, 1965, in the Truman Presidential Library, with Pres. Harry S. Truman at his side, he signed the bills into law. This event would become the action that would save the University of Kentucky Medical Center as we know it today. All those "no-pay" patients suddenly had a financial sponsor and, therefore, additional access to health care.

By going to Independence to sign the bills, Johnson was paying tribute to Truman, who had attempted to get universal health care passed twenty years earlier. I remember Truman's trying to get "socialized medicine" started. Up until the end of World War II, medical care in the United States was typically "fee-for-service." But in Great Britain and France, doctors and hospitals were under government control during the war—the people and doctors liked it and didn't want to go back to fee-for-service. Germany, since the time of Bismarck in the 1890s, had provided government health care.

As a college sophomore in 1948-49, I took the required course Social Science Studies (sociology, political science and economics), in which our teacher, Gladys Pieper, had us debate (after study and preparation) "Resolved: to establish socialized medicine in the U.S." I was the only student to take the pro side. My classmates couldn't understand why I made that choice. I think I did it then just to be different, but I believe that today most college students would take "my" side.

The passage of Medicare and Medicaid in 1965 dashed the plans of Dr. Willard to create a new kind of medical school—a school focused on being a referral hospital to demonstrate exemplary total patient care and to train primary care doctors. However, the patient-care needs were so great and now that Kentucky residents had some access, the hospital simply could not maintain a narrow teaching purpose. So, because of the continuing huge immediate patient-care needs, we have become a large regional primary-secondary-tertiary care hospital for all of Eastern and Central Kentucky.

Initially, we had a small Emergency Room of approximately 500 square feet. Our new Emergency Room, which opened in July, 2010, will be approximately the size of a football field. Improvements in our laboratories, imaging techniques, drugs, and treatments, combined with our growing understanding of diseases, would not allow us to keep the simple goal of 1960. Succeeding leaders have seen and reacted to the new needs and possibilities. We began with public health professionals and progressed to clinical doctors in leadership roles, leaders who can focus on a single sick person and not just the general health needs of masses of people. We are always scrambling to keep up. As we need to be.

We have broadened our target to include the people with no or impaired access to care. In the next months and years, health-care reform, in whatever form it comes, will continue to bring more patients to our doors and provide more human laboratories to educate and train more doctors, including specialists and subspecialists.

><+ ><+

In 1960, not many people in Kentucky had health insurance. Blue Cross-Blue Shield was insuring more and more families. A few private health insurance companies, such as Mutual of Omaha, were also just getting off the ground. But at that time, hospital and doctor bills were quite low. The start-up of Blue Cross was described by then-Business Editor Jim Jordan in a 1987 *Lexington Herald-Leader* article:

> **Baylor University's faculty made a landmark deal with a Dallas hospital in the late 1920s.**
>
> The teachers agreed to pay $6 each a month, and the hospital promised to provide, at no additional cost, a semi-private room for up to 21 days a year for all members of the group who needed hospital care. The plan worked. The idea of paying in advance for health care spread rapidly around the country, reaching the Bluegrass by 1938, when the non-profit corporation that eventually would become Blue Cross and Blue Shield of Kentucky was founded.

Numerous other private health care companies have come and gone to and from Kentucky over the past 50 years. Now that universal health care insurance has passed and is still under full debate, one wonders how Kentucky's children (zero-18 years) are doing. For this estimate, I consulted our College of Public Health. Julia F. Costich, J.V., Ph.D., and director of the MHA Program in the Department of Public Health Services Management, replied:

> The attached pie chart is based on Table HIA5 of the 2009 Census Bureau report estimating the number of Kentucky children by coverage category. Kentucky Medicaid reports 447,592 enrolled children as of December 2009, an increase of more than 86,000 from the Census figure. However, given the loss of parental employer-sponsored coverage in the intervening period, a large but unknown proportion of the gain in Medicaid coverage is offset by loss in the commercial sector. Census data on Medicaid enrollment are also consistently lower than state counts for a number of technical reasons. We can estimate that about 9 percent of Kentucky children remain uninsured.

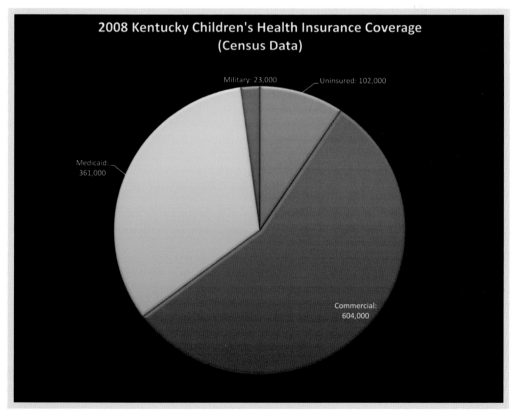

Pie chart showing third-party coverage for children in Kentucky.
Illustration Courtesy of Julia Costich.

Given the fact that, in 1960, private insurance like Blue Cross-Blue Shield did not insure neonates (from birth to 30 days) and employer-sponsored coverage was rare, there was an effort by insurance companies to keep expenses and premiums low. To "limit adverse risk selection," they excluded coverage of relatively predictable medical events such as pregnancy and newborn care. In theory, these were conditions that one should be able to budget for. Somewhere in the 1970s, the American Academy of Pediatrics started a campaign for states to adopt laws that require insurers to cover both maternal and newborn care. Kentucky was successful in doing so. Kentucky's children are actually much better off in 2010 than they were in 1960. Our goal, whatever the mechanism, should be that all children be given all they need to grow up healthy.

CHAPTER 12

New Wind from Texas

A break in the long information-less wait for a new leader came in November 2004, when Dean Jay Perman set up a special luncheon for all the pediatric faculty to meet our new chairman. A quick Google search found J. Timothy Bricker, M.D., to be a well-credentialed pediatric cardiologist, the pediatric right-hand of renowned Houston heart surgeon Michael DeBakey. At the luncheon, he presented himself as a soft-spoken leader who talked of bringing good health care to all of Kentucky's children—nothing you could grumble about.

Our next sighting of Bricker came at our loud annual Christmas party for all faculty and staff. He stood quietly in a brown suit with vest, observing from a side door. He reminded me of Dustin Hoffman in *Kramer vs. Kramer,* sitting on a straight chair in the middle of a Christmas office party swirling around him and not knowing anyone. Of course, the situations for Bricker and Hoffman were quite different. Bricker had the job. We finally had a new pediatric chairman.

J. Timothy Bricker, M.D., MBA
Ohio State, M.D., 1976
University of Chicago, MBA, 2002
Chairman, 2004-present

KENTUCKY CHILDREN'S HOSPITAL

During the next weeks, we began to learn more about this Ohio Quaker, frequently seen in a scrubsuit tending post-operative heart patients through the night. There is a permanent air mattress in his office where he sleeps in order to be available to those children, but the next day he is in his suit, vest, and tie—where does he clean up? New faculty began arriving, and he was present at conferences. Then

the big move—he changed our logo and name of the hospital. No longer was it the University of Kentucky Children's Hospital, but the Kentucky Children's Hospital. The meaning of the name change indicated that our

The new Kentucky Children's Hospital logo.

hospital no longer belonged to the University of Kentucky or to the Department of Pediatrics; rather, it belonged to all of Kentucky's children and those who take care of children here.

Tim Bricker had moved the cheese, and if a mouse was to survive, he'd better figure out to where the cheese had been moved—better and more comprehensive service—any child who needs hospitalization should be in Kentucky Children's Hospital because here is the place to obtain advanced medical care.

Members of the first Kentucky Children's Hospital Board of Directors in 2006 include, seated left to right: Sheila David, Susie Merida, Kim Rosenstein, Carol Gardner, and Missy Scanlon. Standing, left to right: Tim Bricker, Anne Thomas, Ralph Coldiron, Connie Joiner, Luther Deaton, Jim Richardson, Nana Mensah, Jennifer Mynear, and Jane Warner. Not pictured: Jim Elliott, Karen Brooks, Ken Rush, Greg David, Robert Canada, and Dan Martin.
Courtesy of Lee P. Thomas Photography, Inc.

HOPSCOTCH

I first appreciated the changing image of our department and hospital one morning when I got off the elevator and saw 10-inch hopscotch cat's-paws in the corridor leading up to the doors of our children's clinic. All of us enjoy watching children—preschoolers to high schoolers—hopscotch their way into and out of clinic. The next image change was STITCHES, a large mascot for children, big or small, who is always at group events, on the wards, and at awards.

Stitches, the pediatric mascot, with a young patient.

Then a gift allowed for reorganization of University Hospital's Emergency Room to have a special pediatric area of the existing ER; now there is a new and separate ER just for infants and children, opened in August 2010—a major recognition of the special medical needs and treatment of children.

ADDITIONS AND REVISIONS

Makenna David Pediatric Emergency Center is in honor of Makenna David. While being treated in hospital ER rooms, Greg and Sheila David experienced emergency department waiting rooms and facilities with Makenna and their other children. Their gift

The Makenna David Foundation, named after the daughter of Sheila and Greg David, helped identify the need for both the current and the new, larger children's emergency center, and the foundation also provided funding for the two centers. The new center, opened July 14, 2010, is the only dedicated children's emergency center in the state.

Greg and Sheila David and Janice Mueller (far right) stand near the wall honoring the Davids' daughter, Makenna.

Mark Plunkett, M.D., surgical director, Kentucky Children's Heart Center.

through the Makenna David Foundation encouraged the leaders of the Kentucky Children's Hospital to create an ER just for children. Already, a part of our existing ER has been adapted for this purpose, with eight rooms, specialized equipment and staff—a level-1 trauma center. When the new mammoth ER was opened in 2010, the Makenna David Center contained at least 12 beds and separate areas for triage, waiting, and care under direction of a full-time emergency care physician, Dr. Craig Carter, with more being recruited.

Kentucky Children's Heart Center. What is a Center? The dictionary tells us: "a point, area, person, or thing that is most important or pivotal in relation to an indicated activity, interest or condition." This definition does not do justice to what we are really talking about. In February 2010, the *Pittsburgh Gazette* reported how the University of Pittsburgh's transplant team, members of different departments and divisions, came together to perform a double hand transplant. They planned together as if they were developing a Super Bowl game plan. They used a strategy of collaboration to face the complexity of medical care needed, then walked through their assignments, and finally were able to perform. It was *teamwork,* and they were successful. Our Children's Heart Center will function the same way.

The creation of the center—in this, the Heart Center—begins with leading physicians. Mark Plunkett, M.D., is chief of Pediatric Cardiothoracic Surgery and a co-director of Kentucky Children's Heart Center, who received his M.D. at the University of North Carolina in Chapel Hill, N.C. He had further training at Duke University in Durham, N.C., and UCLA in Los Angeles. Describing his team in the fall 2009 edition of *UK Medicine,* Plunkett said: "We've got the expertise in place or being put into place to take care of any child with any heart defect, regardless of its complexity. We also take care of adults who have had congenital heart disease since childhood, which is a very rapidly growing population. A lot of heart defects are discovered early in the pregnancy, so we can plan a course of action for when the mother is going to deliver. In the old days, we talked to the parents after the baby was born; now we're talking to pregnant moms and performing procedures sometimes within days of birth—many within the first week or two of life."

The surgical team specializes in early correction or complete repair of single-ventricle heart defects and a wide range of congenital heart diseases. In addition, valvular repair or replacement in children is an increasingly common procedure, as are follow-up procedures for adults who had heart disease as children. The newest heart surgeon member of the team is Debra Kozik, D.O.

Another key member of the team is Louis Bezold, M.D., the chief of Pediatric Cardiology and also a co-director of Kentucky Children's Heart Center. Bezold earned his M.D. at the University of Maryland, Baltimore. In the fall 2009 edition of *UK Medicine*, Bezold said: "We can essentially identify all complex congenital heart diseases in the fetus. This information helps us plan the rest of the pregnancy and follow-up, and we can intervene immediately if necessary. Parents of babies delivered here have already had the opportunity to meet with a neonatologist, so they're not getting blind-sided."

The team provides services covering a wide range of cardiac specialties, including electrophysiology for arrhythmia detection and treatment; pacemaker implantation and management; interventional cardiac catheterization; and subspecialty expertise in heart failure/cardiomyopathy, preventive cardiology, and pulmonary hypertension. They perform a variety of non-invasive procedures, including pediatric and fetal echocardiography.

Other members of the team include J. Timothy Bricker, M.D., MBA; Carol Cottrill, M.D.; Thomas DiSessa, M.D.; Bahram Kakavand, M.D.; Jacqueline A. Noonan, M.D.; and Mark Vranicar, M.D.

"It's unusual for a physician group like ours to offer subspecialty coverage in so many areas," Bezold said. "We offer coverage in all important areas of pediatric cardiology."

These cardiologists depend heavily on expertise in anesthesiology, and the Kentucky Children's Hospital team is led by Raeford E. Brown, Jr., M.D., and chief of Pediatric Anesthesiology, who received his M.D. at the University of North Carolina in Chapel Hill, along with further training at Children's Hospital National Medical Center in Washington, D.C., and the University of Virginia in Charlottesville. His staff includes Eugene Hessel, M.D.; Thomas Murphy, M.D.; and Randall Schell, M.D.

Brown, who was quoted in *UK Medicine*'s fall 2009 edition, said, "We have a continuum of highly skilled and talented clinicians to manage every step in what is a very sophisticated dance to improve the

Louis Bezold, M.D., medical director, Kentucky Children's Heart Center.

Tim Bricker, M.D., pediatric cardiologist, holding a congenital heart patient who was operated on successfully.

lives of these infants. The people that care for these children see themselves as advocates for children. We treat them like they're our own, and we care for them just as we think the parents would care for them. We try to have a small number of people who take care of these infants on a regular basis. There are only a few clinicians in Kentucky who have the training and expertise to manage them in the operating room, and we're lucky to have them."

UK Medicine, in its fall 2009 edition, summed up the Kentucky Children's Heart Center thusly: "Top-notch medical expertise combined with a healthy dose of leading-edge technology and compassionate teamwork are proving to be an effective recipe for treating sick children at UK HealthCare's Kentucky Children's Heart Center. The heart center is quickly developing a reputation as the region's premier comprehensive care center for children with heart disease, even as the medical team continues to push toward even higher levels of care that someday may include cardiac transplantation."

Newborn Screening

Newborn screening (NBS) for metabolic, endocrine, and pulmonary disorders, developed over the past half century, has been the most significant advance in public health during this time period. NBS is now practiced in all 50 states and in most industrialized countries.

NBS screening for phenylketonuria (Guthrie bacterial inhibition assay) was started in Kentucky in 1966. Galactosemia (fluorometric assay) was added in 1978, followed by congenital hypothyroidism (submicro thyroid hormone T_4 and thyroid stimulating hormone TSH) in 1980. To this battery of three, gel electrophoresis for sickle cell anemia was added in 1986. By 1990, this was the entire battery of newborn screening tests that all states were using.

Tandem mass spectrometry (MS-MS) was developed to analyze acylcarnitines in the 1980s: the technique was extended to newborn screening by the development of

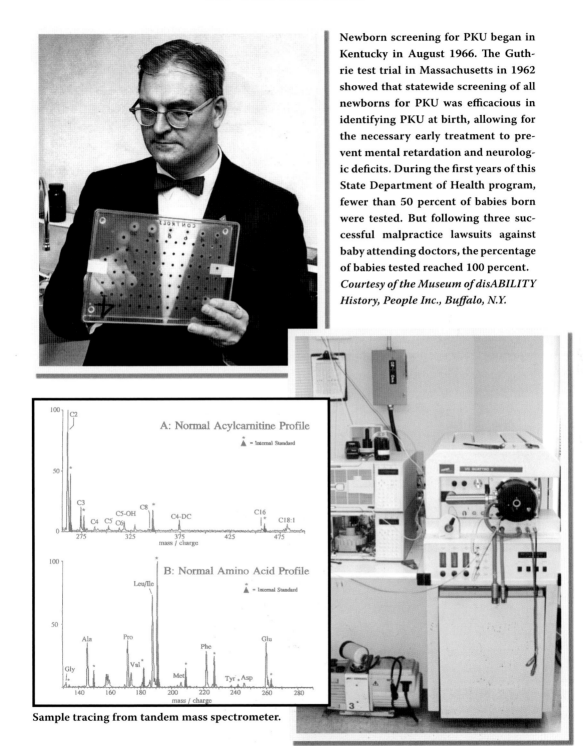

Newborn screening for PKU began in Kentucky in August 1966. The Guthrie test trial in Massachusetts in 1962 showed that statewide screening of all newborns for PKU was efficacious in identifying PKU at birth, allowing for the necessary early treatment to prevent mental retardation and neurologic deficits. During the first years of this State Department of Health program, fewer than 50 percent of babies born were tested. But following three successful malpractice lawsuits against baby attending doctors, the percentage of babies tested reached 100 percent. *Courtesy of the Museum of disABILITY History, People Inc., Buffalo, N.Y.*

Sample tracing from tandem mass spectrometer.

Tandem mass spectrometer, 2005 to present.

automated techniques of sample preparation, injection into the instrument and analysis of results. By using MS-MS, amino acids, organic acids, and some enzymes can be identified and measured in body fluids.

Some research laboratories began to identify and to measure these metabolic compounds, allowing for the diagnoses of many rare metabolic diseases. Massachusetts and Maryland were the first states to add eight to 10 congenital metabolic disorders to their state screening panel, and others began to follow suit.

By 2001, it had become obvious that all states should expand the number of disorders they screened for. Bill HR 4365 to provide federal funding for expanded newborn screening in all states made its way through Congress, passed in the U.S. Senate in December 2000, and was sent to the U.S. House of Representatives. There the Health and Welfare Subcommittee passed HR 4365 and sent it to the Congressional Budget Office to determine the cost of expanded newborn screening for the approximately 4 million newborns each year. Rumors had it calculated at $50 for each baby. The bill was scheduled for an up or down vote in the House before Congress adjourned September 30, 2001.

After the terrorist assault by Al Qaeda occurred on September 11, 2001, all the bills scheduled for action from that day through September 30, 2001, were abandoned, most likely never to be considered again.

In 2003, I began working with a family who had lost a 20-month-old son as a crib death (SIDS) who proved to have VLCAD (very long chain CoA dehydrogenase deficiency) and showed the characteristic myocardiopathy and other findings of the disorder. The disorder was confirmed by analyzing frozen tissue that the pathologist had saved when he performed the autopsy. Energized by these parents, I began retracing my steps at the State Capitol that had resulted in passage of the mandated coverage of medical formulas in 2003.

This time I wanted to avoid some of my past

Ron Whitley, a laboratory colleague, and Carol Reid, newborn screening coordinator, are essential team members of the Expanded Newborn Screening Program.

Tim Bricker, chairman of the UK Department of Pediatrics, spoke with Bill Hacker, Kentucky Commissioner of Health, at the dedication of the Expanded Newborn Screening Program.

mistakes. I talked with Rep. Robert Damron (D-39th), who told me that if I could get the bill out of both the Senate and House Health and Welfare committees that it would sweep through both the Senate and House chambers. At that point, I became an advocate, though I had no perks or money to distribute. This was a full-time job for a semi-retired pediatrician. There were 12 senators on the Senate Health and Welfare Committee chaired by Sen. Julie Denton (R-34th) and 16 representatives on the House Health and Welfare Committee chaired by Tom Burch (D-30th). Encouraged by Sen. Denton, who had come to know the parents of the 20-month-old child who had died of VLCAD, I was able to make my pitch for expanded newborn screening to almost all of the members of the two committees. I could never get more than two meetings scheduled on the same day, so I was in Frankfort many days in January and February 2005. Representative Damron passed me in the halls of the Capitol Annex frequently and would wave—knowing what I was doing. Senate Bill 24 passed by an overwhelming margin in both the Senate and the House.

Next came implementation of SB 24. Dr. Steve Davis formed and led a task force to guide the State Health Department that met frequently throughout the spring and summer of 2005. Finally, in April 2005, I met with Sen. Dan Kelly, majority floor leader in the Senate, when there was wavering on inclusion of cystic fibrosis in the battery of tests. The meeting was arranged by Mrs. Tondreau, a grandmother of one of Dr. Mike Anstead's CF patients; she played Scrabble with the Kellys on Friday nights.

This time the state Health Department was very helpful. Dr. Davis showed Gov. Ernie Fletcher where the $1 million was needed for start-up, including purchase of two tandem mass spectrometers (one to be online and a backup since it had to run every day to examine approximately 200-250 newborn specimens, a spot of blood on filter paper). The laboratory became operational on December 5, 2005.

The 29 disorders tested for—more than any other state at the time—included the following:

Phenylketonuria (PKU)

Sickle cell disease

Congenital hypothyroidism

Galactosemia

Medium-chain acyl-CoA dehydrogenase deficiency (MCAD)

Very long-chain acyl-CoA dehydrogenase deficiency (VLCAD)

Short-chain acyl-CoA dehydrogenase deficiency (SCAD)

Maple syrup urine disease (MSUD)

Congenital adrenal hyperplasia (CAH)

Biotinidase disorder

Cystic fibrosis (CF)

3-methylcrotonyl-CoA carboxylase deficiency (3MCC)

3-OH 3-CH3 glutaric aciduria (HMG)

Argininosuccinic acidemia (ASA)

Beta-ketothiolase deficiency (BKT)

Carnitine uptake deficiency (CUD)

Citrullinemia (CIT)

Glutaric acidemia type I (GA I)

Hb S/beta-thalassemia (Hb S/Th)

Hb S/C disease (Hb S/C)

Homocystinuria (HCY)

Isovaleric acidemia (IVA)

Long-chain L-3-OH acyl-CoA dehydrogenase deficiency (LCAD)

Methylmalonic acidemia (Cbl A,B)

Methylmalonic acidemia mutase deficiency (MUT)

Multiple carboxylase deficiency (MCD)

Propionic acidemia (PA)

Trifunctional protein deficiency (TFP)

Tyrosinemia type I (TYR 1)

More recently, this list has been expanded to 42 by subdividing those that have a subtype, such as Tyrosinemia I and Tyrosinemia II. In Tyrosinemia type I, there is early acute liver failure, renal tubalopathy, neuropathy, and life-threatening crises. On the other hand, Tyrosinemia II is a non-fatal disorder but with painful corneal lesions,

Charlton Mabry, M.D., with an older baby whose blood was tested in the Expanded Newborn Testing Program.

The *Lexington Herald-Leader* reported on the first two babies detected by Kentucky's Expanded Newborn Screening Program, which began testing actual babies' blood on filter paper on Dec. 5, 2005. Both babies are from Cynthiana, Ky. The baby at left has Medium Chain Acyl CoA dehydrogenase deficiency (MCAD), and the baby at right has Very Long Chain Acyl CoA dehydrogenase deficiency (VLCAD). Untreated, 25 percent result in crib deaths from hypoglycemia; untreated survivors have various disabilities. *Photo courtesy of the Lexington Herald-Leader.*

hyperkeratosis of soles and palms, and mild mental retardation. The urgency is less with Tyrosinemia II, but much greater with Tyrosinemia I.

To date, we have been rescuing about 100 babies in our half of the state each year from mental retardation, handicapping conditions, disabilities, or death. I note that NBS alerts the families early that their baby has a medical problem—a problem that can be treated. This early diagnosis saves the family from the medical odyssey of seeking the diagnosis and treatment of their baby or child who may already have incurred mental retardation or some other debilitating condition.

RESEARCH

At the outset, the Department had four M.D.s with working research laboratories:

- Githens—transplant pathology
- Hathaway—coagulation mechanisms
- Mabry—inborn errors of metabolism
- Nelson—allergic plant library

We were individual investigators working at the bench with our patients as problem feeders. But after Medicaid passage, we were expected to do more clinical work, as I have related.

Late on a winter day in 1972, Dr. Dorothy Hollingsworth and I were sitting in my lab (MN 475) lamenting the fact that the National Institutes of Health was moving away from individual investigator grants to group grants with much larger financial support. The University was going along with this change in direction because its overhead for each grant had climbed to 50 to 100 percent. Our new chairman, Dr. Noonan, stopped, leaned against the door frame, listened, then chirped, "clinical dollars spend as well as research dollars"—then buzzed off. Weeks later, Dean William Jordan made it official: "laboratories are for Ph.D.s; clinics and wards are for M.D.s."

Along with this policy change, our Department's contributions to the regional and national meetings of the Society for Pediatric Research (young Turks) and the national meeting of the American Pediatric Society (old Turks) fell off dramatically, and we continue to have only an occasional department member elected to one of these prestigious societies. Most of our outside research support now comes from private funds (e.g. American Cancer Society, American Heart Society, etc.).

In 1963, our new chairman, Vipul Mankad, attempted to jump-start a renewal of laboratory research. He hired a young pediatrician, John Fowlkes, M.D., who came with a NIH grant to study the mechanism of growth hormone function. He remodeled rooms MN 475 and 477 into one updated laboratory with the needed equipment. Later, he left to head the Division of Pediatric Endocrinology at the University of Arkansas Medical School in Little Rock.

Soon afterward, Mankad recruited a pediatric cardiologist who was well-funded for his chick congenital heart model. He remained for only a short time before moving on to be the chief of pediatric cardiology at Pittsburgh Children's Hospital.

The next move came when the Barnstable-Brown Foundation offered money to set up investigations into juvenile diabetes. David Brown, the husband of one of the Barnstable twins, who were then UK cheerleaders and are now celebrities, was disabled with complications of his juvenile diabetes. These monies led to the creation of the Kentucky Pediatric Research Institute (KPRI).

Dr. Bricker describes the KPRI and its rationale:

> *Over the past six years we have developed a Kentucky Pediatric Research Institute (KPRI) to leverage existing strengths of the University of Kentucky and previous investments in research excellence. Even in larger pediatric departments, success of building research programs division-by-division has been very limited in areas of high clinical demand. This is especially true with the number of one or two faculty divisions in the Department of Pediatrics. The KPRI is the Division of Research of the Department of Pediatrics, whose charge is to enhance research opportunities and support across the Department of Pediatrics and throughout the Kentucky Children's Hospital.*
>
> *The KPRI was designed to encompass six core activities. Each of these areas was identified because of the broad applicability to pediatric health, as well as the access to current University strength.*
>
> *The Obesity and Diabetes Research Core and the Pediatric Inflammatory Biology Core were the highest initial priorities. The former has developed well-funded research programs in cell signaling and intracellular messaging. Although crucial to understanding diabetes in youth, many of the basic techniques are applicable to other pediatric diseases. Translational work with proteomic markers of diabetes and pre-diabetes in children and school-based diabetes prevention intervention have been among the projects from this core recently funded by the National Institutes of Health. Inflammation biology has wide-ranging importance in pediatric diseases in many specialties. We grew expertise in this area from recruitment of a new faculty member (into a first tenure-track job) who now has RO1-NIH funding and is collaborating with clinical faculty members of several divisions of the Department of Pediatrics.*

Our Pediatric Cancer Core works most closely with the College of Pharmacy in the new drug development and new pharmacologic mechanisms. We have also addressed pediatric cancer prevention with basic work on the biology of melanin production in the KPRI.

The Pediatric Health Policy Core addresses health outcomes at the population level in concert with the Martin School of Public Policy and faculty from the College of Public Health. Close collaboration with the Kentucky Injury Prevention Research Program and the Center for Study of Violence Against Children is included in this core.

The Clinical Studies Core is designed to provide logistic, technical, and statistical support for young investigators as well as research mentorship and critique. This component has links to the College of Public Health and to the Clinical Research Center of the College of Medicine. Well-developed clinical research programs exist in pediatric oncology, in cystic fibrosis, pediatric orthopedics, and in neonatology. A proposed Molecular Pediatrics Core is a longer-term recruitment priority.

The Kentucky Pediatric Research Institute is now fourth of all clinical Departments and Centers at the University of Kentucky for NIH funding and third when primary and collaborative NIH support is considered. We now lead all but two of the Departments (both in the Basic Sciences) in dollars per full-time investigator and are quite high for dollars per square foot of laboratory space. The Department of Pediatrics and the KPRI have taken advantage of the number of opportunities at the University of Kentucky to provide formal didactic training to young investigators, including several who have recently completed graduate degrees and several currently enrolled. The KPRI has been responsible for success in growth of faculty research in critical care pediatrics, pediatric endocrinology, pediatric nephrology, pediatric pulmonology, and neonatology among new clinical faculty recruitments over the past six years.

><- >←

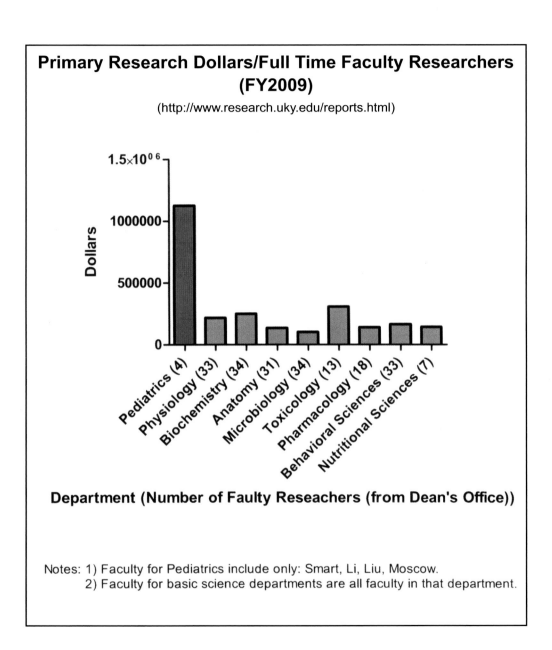

Primary Research Dollars/Full Time Faculty Researchers (FY2009)

(http://www.research.uky.edu/reports.html)

Department (Number of Faulty Reseachers (from Dean's Office))

Notes: 1) Faculty for Pediatrics include only: Smart, Li, Liu, Moscow.
   2) Faculty for basic science departments are all faculty in that department.

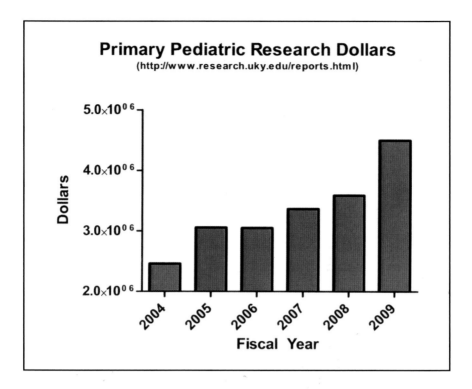

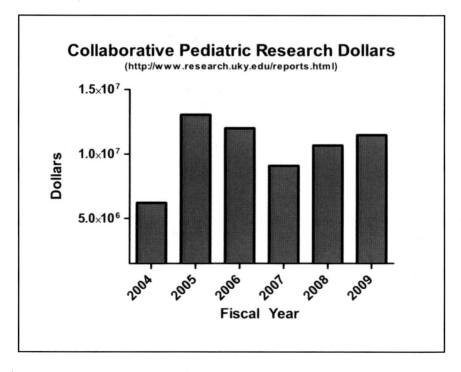

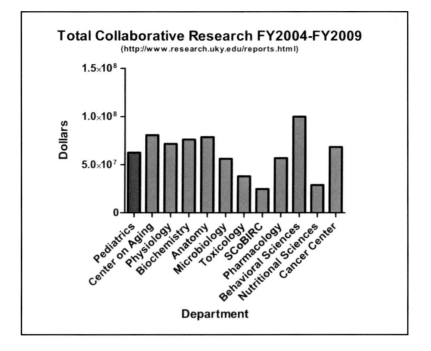

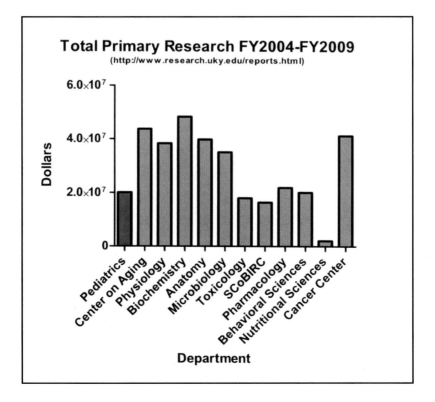

THE CHAIR

What does it mean to be the Chairman of Pediatrics? Abraham Jacobi, the father of American pediatrics, was never a chairman—just a physician who limited his practice to children. As departments of pediatrics began to grow in the university-related hospitals on the East Coast, when they had more than a couple of pediatricians, someone had to be the designated leader—to deal with administrators if nothing else.

I'm reminded of the story of the first chairman of pediatrics at the University of South Carolina in Charleston, a story told to me by Jack Rhoads, M.D., who was the base pediatrician at Camp Lejeune, N.C., during the Korean Conflict. I was a U.S. Navy doctor assigned to a Marine battalion, but was only needed for Monday morning "sick call." So I got myself TAD (temporary additional duty) to the children's ward at the Dependents' Addition at the base hospital. I wasn't yet a trained pediatrician.

Jack's mentor, after graduating from medical school in Charleston, became a pediatric "resident physician" in New York City for two years in the 1930s. Then Mylnor Wilbur Beach, M.D., returned to Charleston, and became a "board certified" pediatrician. He was of similar vintage as Lexington pediatricians Richard Elliott and Robert Warfield. At about the same time, Dr. Beach became chairman of the Department of Pediatrics at the South Carolina School of Medicine in 1942. Previously, pediatrics was a division of the Department of Medicine. His assigned hospital territory was two beds on the Negro Women's Medical Ward in the city public hospital. If there were more than two admissions of babies, he placed them sideways in the two beds. But they made it work. Jack, a second-generation Charleston pediatrician, was proud of his mentor.

My first experience with a Department of Pediatrics chairman was with Richard Blumberg, the chairman at Emory University School of Medicine in Atlanta. Dick Blumberg was unmarried and seemed to devote his whole life to pediatrics; he received no university salary but, instead, supported himself by maintaining a private practice in a downtown office in the afternoons. Twenty-eight years later, he designated me as medical alumni AOA member, in recognition of my pediatric research efforts and publications. Although there were a number of geographic full-time pediatric faculty by this time, he always maintained his private office. His eventual replacement was a neonatologist, Al Brann, who came on board after the department moved from downtown Grady Hospital to the on-campus Henrietta Eggleston Children's Hospital. Brann also was recognized as a successful chairman and is still working on the excessive premature birth problem.

Next, after fulfilling my Navy doctor-draft time, I began a pediatric residency under Waldo E. Nelson, M.D., at St. Christopher's Hospital for Children, Temple University in Philadelphia, one of the most sought-after in the country. Though I had heard stories, I was still surprised on July 1, 1957, at 8 a.m. when Dr. Nelson came into the classroom, sized up the nine of us first-year residents, then declared, "Even though eight of you are married, there might still be a possibility that you can become a good resident." He was also quite disappointed that my wife Barbara, an experienced medical editor, was pregnant yet again—and thus unavailable to help with his current edition of *The Textbook of Pediatrics*. Previous classes had all been single, but he was now dealing with some veterans. He expected a great deal for $50 a month stipends. At that point, only inferior training programs paid a salary to get by on.

I later learned that Nelson was the only faculty member of 12 who was paid by Temple University ($25,000 a year), since the other 11 received their salaries through a St. Christopher foundation of wealthy donors and bankers. Years later, when I was being recruited to return to St. Christopher's, at a private night meeting with Angie DiGeorge, Nelson, and me, the general question of salaries came up. At one point, Nelson told Angie, "I don't remember how much you were paid, but I do remember how you were paid." For each of us residents, Nelson quickly learned our pluses and minuses, for he took a personal interest in learning who we were, and he enjoyed challenging us individually. We all ate in the basement cafeteria, and we tried to sit near Nelson at a large table to hear his stories and comments. All males—we were a close group.

Everyone was always greatly impressed that he was the editor of the most revered textbook, *Nelson's Textbook of Pediatrics*, now in its 20th edition. It continues to carry his name long after his retirement, for, until his death, he picked the new editors. I remember that when he was in the hospital for an inquinal hernia repair, I was the designated resident to carry a box of the just-released edition of *Nelson's Textbook* to his bedside so he could begin signing copies for the contributors. I got the first signed copy of that edition, which still has an honored spot in my bookcase today. He told me the origin of this text. It began in 1929 at Tulane (New Orleans Charity Hospital) when Dr. Graham wrote the first edition. For the next few editions, he was joined by Dr. Mitchell, who later moved on to the University of Cincinnati (Cincinnati Children's Hospital) where Mitchell was the sole editor. On his deathbed, Dr. Mitchell called Nelson and asked him to assume the editorship, for he knew Nelson, who formerly had been on faculty at Cincinnati Children's Hospital and a co-editor for two editions.

Nelson's Textbook of Pediatrics was a continuous work with little down time between editions. The book was perpetually laid out on the Nelsons' windowed side porch where Mrs. Nelson could help out. Since he habitually worked on it on Sundays, he never mentioned going to church. Dr. Nelson was a giant in pediatrics, not for his scientific discoveries or breakthroughs, but for his organizational abilities, creation of a top-rated training program that attracted young people from home and abroad, and for the textbook.

The saddest appointment of a chairman was at another medical school when a Nobel Prize recipient was made chairman of his department largely because of the Nobel Prize. His clinical faculty literally killed him with their daily demands—he died of a heart attack from the stress.

The nicest and most thoughtful St. Christopher's professor I knew was Victor Vaughan. He went to the University of Georgia in Athens as their Chairman of Pediatrics. Coming from main-line Philadelphia, he was just not ready for the culture shock of Georgia cracker culture. He was back to St. Christopher in just a few years as Dr. Nelson's first replacement. Some predicted that going to Kentucky, perched on the edge of Appalachia, could be similar for me. But they didn't realize that having grown up in Knoxville, a large Appalachian city would not be culture shock to me.

The leadership situation for start-up Kentucky was a stable one with a known salary scale. If you were energetic and original, you could find outside support, and initially had time to do what was necessary to get outside support. But with the clinical overload that began in the mid-1960s, we started a rapid turnover of chairmen in other departments. This was abetted by the appointment of John Oswald as our new University president in the late 1960s. He ruled that there would be no lifetime chairman appointments— six years in the Medical School and four years throughout the rest of the University.

Interestingly, the chairman appointment schedule of six years was not enforced in Pediatrics. Dr. Noonan's appointment was unique since she was the first female chair, and it looked as if we were moving forward. At the end of her third six-year term (18 years), we were in the doldrums with few resources. Her personal style and energy made up for a lot.

Noonan's departure as chairman set the stage for our next chairman, Vipul Mankad, who brought hope for a children's hospital and new money. He left after 11 years, because of the doldrums again, I think. And this time, the Wethington University administration was winding down.

Dr. Tim Bricker, Physician-in-Chief, leads Kentucky Children's Hospital in its mission to improve the lives and health of children and to provide a more optimistic future for their families.

✷✻ ✻✷

In 2002, Lee Todd, a native Kentuckian, UK College of Engineering graduate, and a successful entrepreneur, became our University president, and things began to change. Along with President Todd's new development plan came a restructuring of the Medical Center's administration and a change in administrative personnel. Dr. Michael Karpf, who had been involved in restructuring of the UCLA medical center in Los Angeles, was appointed Executive Vice President for the Medical Center. He reported to Dr. Todd that he had looked at all the top-twenty medical schools and medical centers in the country, and that they were all BIG. He asserted that he could not lift a small medical school and center into the top twenty and stay small—we must go BIG. Dr. Todd gave him the go-ahead key to becoming a top-twenty school, which would be bringing "advanced care" to Kentucky; this would require a dependence on clinical subspecialists as well as an enlargement of our research effort.

Bringing along our Department of Pediatrics to be rated in the top twenty of all other departments of pediatrics (129 schools) is Dr. Bricker's charge and challenge. This includes Dr. Karpf's mantra that *no Kentuckian shall have to cross the state line to get the best of care.* Karpf expects it.

Remember, in 1962 we began with two beds on 3-East; take a look below at our statistics for 2009:

Pediatrics
Total Beds

NICU beds... 66

PICU beds 12

Acute care beds 44

23-hour observation............................ 11

Total beds 133

Visits

Inpatient.. 4,715

NICU 806

Outpatient 58,955

Obstetrics
Newborn nursery admissions 1,643

What will these stats look like in 2060? The most predictable fact is that our patient catchment area is expected to contain between 500,000 to 1 million more people than it now does. Babies and children a'plenty. But maybe, with designer babies a strong possibility in the future, plain old defects and illnesses may have disappeared. I am sure there will be new ones—even more challenging—and undreamed-of drugs and technologies to enable pediatricians to do battle.

TO THE HOUSESTAFF

This book of history was made possible by the over 600 of you who spent two to four years as a "resident" physician in training every day plus every third night and every third weekend in the hospital. You were the hospital intake physician and the first responder for every baby and child. The post medical school training programs were:

Straight Pediatrics—3 years
Medicine-Pediatrics—4 years
Medicine-Pediatrics-Psychiatry—5 years

The role of the "resident" physician continues to change. Before WWII, there were only a few resident physicians, mostly surgeons. They were single and lived in the hospital. Marriage was deferred. Almost all medical school graduates went directly into General Practice.

After WWII, specialty training programs greatly increased and were expected for all medical school graduates. In my residency group, as I have recounted, 8 of 9 of us were married; most were Korean War veterans. We were allowed to live outside the hospital (with our wives).

Following the Vietnam War, there has been a great influx of international student graduates into our residency programs. The feminist movement of the 1970s brought many women into medical schools; many have chosen pediatrics as their specialty. Along with this entry of women, the sleeping and overnight conditions and work schedules have greatly improved. How all this will evolve in the NEXT FIFTY will be interesting, for undoubtedly, additional time will be added to our training programs. After all, the half-life of a medical fact or treatment plan is only five years and new knowledge has to be factored in.

As Dr. David Clark told us, medicine is different from other professions—"You have to do it to teach it!" Finally, the satisfaction of working and learning together has been our greatest personal reward.

✜ ✜ ✜

In 2007, the Department of Pediatrics and University of Kentucky Children's Hospital established an honor entitled "Distinguished Service Lifetime Achievement Award" to recognize the "lifetime achievement" of its physicians. To date the following individuals have been recognized:

2007-2008　C. Charlton Mabry, M.D. Endocrinology, Metabolism

2008-2009　Nirmala Desai, M.D. Neonatology

2009-2010　Bryan Hall, M.D. Genetics, Dysmorphology

AFTERWORD

Looking back over these 50 years, I have come to realizations I might never have had without the challenge of writing this book. Most importantly, I now understand that a mid-course correction allowed us to become a significant medical school with the potential to break into the top tier. Evolving in response to pressure from our constituents—away from the "ideal" medical school of our dreaming early planners—left us room to continue to grow with the times.

In the 1970s, Dr. Peter Bosomworth, our new medical chancellor, first opened up and enlarged our emergency room, and patients poured in; he also fostered the development of the Neonatal Intensive Care Unit—another timely answer to a growing need. These two steps forward signified our willingness to use our facilities and staff to meet the needs of babies and children in the region.

Our first three deans happened to be academic public health specialists, and our next six were academic clinical practitioners. Their energy and concerns, their biases and agenda, all necessarily shaped the direction of the department. Meanwhile, we doctors in the trenches took care of our small charges—who came from the coal fields and the tobacco fields, the mountains and the towns, and the bluegrass of Eastern and Central Kentucky. And they keep coming.

We soon learned to capitalize on our location on the edge of Appalachia, discovering a mother lode of genetic disorders in Eastern Kentucky—most likely because of its long history of consanguinity. An isolated people of English, Scotch-Irish, and German ancestry, Appalachians and other rural patients invited our interest in medical genetics. Therefore, we not only have a Division of Genetics but also an interest in genetic involvement in other illnesses throughout all the divisions in the department. Probably 90 percent of the entries in the latest (1998) edition of Dr. Victor McKusick's *Mendelian Inheritance in Man, A Catalogue of Human Genes and Genetic Disorders* are from pediatric literature. Our many publications on these disorders have substantially enlarged the literature. We thus continue to be a research and teaching institution in spite of our vastly enlarged patient service.

Finally, there are everyday heroes, our pediatric resident physicians, women and men. In these first 50 years, 600 medical school graduates have trained on our fourth floor—straight pediatrics, medicine-pediatrics, and triple board (pediatrics, medicine-pediatrics, child psychiatry). These are the young doctors who stay "in the house" at bedsides and emergency rooms after the faculty go home, awake most of the time. We are doubly indebted to the 50 chief residents, who out of loyalty or desire to enter academic pediatrics, gave an extra year. Usually they were the best hands-on doctors and kept all the other resident physicians fully engaged in bedside care of our sickest patients—an honor and a huge responsibility. Many have gone on to meaningful academic careers. We salute you.

The pledge, that involves each of us, is that no Kentucky resident will have to cross the state line to receive state-of-the-art health care. We in Pediatrics have been working toward that end for the last 50 years. It would be great to be able to stick around to see how this great effort plays out.

Billy F. Andrews, M.D. (Retired)
Professor and Chairman Emeritus, Department of Pediatrics, University of Louisville,
Kosair Charities Pediatric Center, Louisville, Ky.

When I was asked to write a review and comment for First Fifty—A Pediatric Story by C. Charlton Mabry, M.D. with Barbara Mabry and Jim Niemi, celebrating the fiftieth anniversary of the University of Kentucky, Department of Pediatrics, I felt honored and duty bound to try to do it, especially for Chart Mabry and other friends of longstanding at UK. Chart Mabry had been a friend and colleague since 1960-61, when he helped me with several metabolic problems while I was at Walter Reed Army Institute of Research. Barbara Mabry has been his lifelong love and help in so many ways. She became an English professor, writer, poet, etc. Jim Niemi is a former school teacher, writer, news reporter and interviewer. The current chairman of the Department of Pediatrics, Doctor J. Timothy Bricker, who since 2004 has built a new Kentucky Children's Hospital and added many new services, specialties and faculty, personally charged Doctor Mabry who had been on the original faculty to write the history of the Department of Pediatrics.

Thoughts of what is to come are illustrated from the Frontispiece—a beautiful picture of a tiny foot in an adult's extended open hand inside an incubator. Its statement lets us know that we are in for a real reading treat: "This history is about many strands of activity woven together like a loomed, complexly patterned scarf, revealing some strands ending and others starting or restarting. It is a history written by a weaver as he saw it from the fourth floor of University Hospital and the second floor of Kentucky Clinic. It is a microcosm of all the hospital's activity because, on any given day, 10 to 20 percent of patients were babies and children."

Almost everyone who reads the chapter Signature Patients and other stories about patients like them will enjoy this book. I personally am always proud of the many accomplishments under the hardest circumstances of these stories. They are steeped in the love of the history, ethics, and humanities in medicine. It was good to learn of the growth and contributions of the house staff, especially because some faculty and residents care for Kentucky's children.

The photography is good and effective. The poetry was informative and enjoyable. The "65 roses" was memorable, as was the Frontispiece.

I was greatly pleased to see that the names and works of many of my friends of over a half century from the University of Kentucky and those who have passed on are included. I certainly appreciated all comments from and about my first friends, Doctors Chart Mabry, Warren Wheeler, Jacqueline Noonan, Doan Fischer, Robert Beargie, Vernon James, Nirmala Desai, and Douglas Cunningham. Two of the faculty were from the University of Louisville. Bryan Hall was a graduate of the University of Louisville and one of the greatest chief residents in the past 50 years, and was also one of the greatest diagnosticians who was in on all the most interesting cases and loved children who looked different and genetics. Henrietta Bada-Ellzey completed her pediatrics training and neonatology fellowship at the University of Louisville and was the best in physiology of them all. I anticipate that all who love and care for children will have much to gain from this book.

In our work with children may we remember the great challenge that, "The level of civilization attained by any society will be determined by the attention it has paid to the welfare of its infants and children." I thank you and have enjoyed the opportunity to learn more about these great works for children.

><+ ><

Peter P. Bosomworth, M.D. (Retired)
Founding Chairman of Department of Anesthesiology;
Chancellor of UK Medical Center, 1970-1992, University of Kentucky, Lexington, Ky.

Anyone interested in learning more about the care of infants and children will enjoy reading this book. Dr. Mabry, with the help of his wife and professional colleagues in the Kentucky Children's Hospital, has done a remarkable job of documenting the history, growth, and development of the Department of Pediatrics. The stories are interesting, accurate and entertaining. From a small beginning with limited financial resources, the faculty and staff, over the fifty years, have built a notable program. It incorporates all of the elements of the three leg academic stool—patient care, teaching and research.

One will find humor, poetry, enthusiasm, concern, and caring in their words and accomplishments. Many Kentucky families have benefited from the success of their endeavors. The included pictures and graphics are easily understood. While admitting to some bias, I enjoyed reading this book and expect others will also.

⊱⊰ ⊱⊰

Steve Davis, M.D.
Senior Deputy State Health Officer, Deputy Commissioner,
Kentucky Department for Public Health, Frankfort, Ky.

"Tell it like it is! and yep, they nailed it". From its opening page to its closing paragraph, Dr. Charlton Mabry's First Fifty: A Pediatric Story highlights the "Guiding Principle" held in the hearts of all members of the University of Kentucky, Department of Pediatrics. This time honored "Principle" is that we are a family of faculty, staff, students, residents and children.Without exception the center of our family is that of our children.

Throughout his writing and personal experiences Dr. Mabry is able to capture in touching stories the heartfelt love that the members of the Department of Pediatrics have for the children of Kentucky. The history clearly acknowledges the many complex pediatric conditions that exist and the story unfolds to emphasize that while direct patient care remains paramount the need for teaching and academic research is part of the yellow brick road to improve their lives.

What an accomplishment; the dream of and the birth of both the Department of Pediatrics and the Kentucky Children's Hospital!

Consistent with focusing on the needs of our children, the author shies away from the faculty's absolute marvelous teaching abilities that take young energetic minds and mold them into strong docs, while also reminding the newly trained physician that "The Good Doctor Knows What They Don't Know". The faculty throughout the fifty years began and has remained "a patient's doctor" as well as being admired mentors to all students and resident physicians privileged to serve with them.

Having had the unique opportunity to experience the University of Kentucky Pediatric Department as a medical student, a physician resident, a private practice pediatrician, a state Maternal and Child Health Director and a Deputy State Health Officer, the book brings to me a real-life look at the needs of Kentucky's children and the magnificent efforts the Commonwealth, the Department and the University took to meet these needs over the past Half Century.

Fifty years ago the dream began of a place where children in need of medical care could come and know that they would be the center of the family. The barriers to health care that so many experienced and the visionary leadership to eliminate those barriers helped to bring this dream to a reality. The heart of the University of Kentucky Department of Pediatrics and the Kentucky Children's Hospital beats tirelessly to serve our children day in and day out.

First Fifty: A Pediatric Story is a wonderful read for all who know and love our children. Sprinkled with a dose of "good ole' Kentucky Politics" and woven into a "GIT R' DONE" attitude, this story will not sit idle on your shelf, but will be a "treasure remembered".

>+< >+<

Mary P. Fox, M.D. (Retired)
Graduate of University of Louisville Medical School;
longtime local health department head, Pike County, Pikeville, Ky.

This is a jewel of an in-depth history of an outstanding Pediatric Department and its most successful "Out Reach Clinics".

Do you believe in Angels? I DO! They may appear in many shapes, forms and disguises. The out-reach clinics had two in my esteemed estimation: Dr. Mabry in the Diabetic Clinic and Dr. Jackie Noonan in the Heart Clinic. Eastern Kentucky was isolated many years by lack of good roads. Short distances were hard to travel, let alone long distances. When Dr. Mabry and Dr. Noonan discovered Eastern Kentucky children and came OUT TO THEM—what a blessing that was. I was there!

So many children were seen, diagnosed, treated and grew up healthy because of these angels who came and found them.

Thank you for 50 years of service and the history of those years.

>+< >+<

Al Smith (Retired)
Longtime host of KET's *Comment on Kentucky*, Lexington, Ky.

As the University of Kentucky celebrates 50 years of teaching at its College of Medicine and providing patient service from the hospital of the Albert B. Chandler Medical Center, a story of these five decades has been told by a distinguished physician who was "present at the creation."

This combined memoir and history of the pediatrics program, dedicated to "the children of Kentucky," is a gift to all of us who should want to know the details of an important chapter in the advance of health care in our state.

A candid, comprehensive account, "The First Fifty" by Dr. C. Charlton Mabry is the humanistic perspective of a faculty member who started teaching at the new college and caring for babies and children at its new hospital when the infant mortality rate in Kentucky was 17 babies for every 1000 births. He doesn't claim that the rate has dropped to 7.5 deaths over 50 years solely because of the progress of the pediatric program at the college and what is now called the Kentucky Children's Hospital, but there is no question that he and his colleagues made a tremendous contribution to the treatment of children (and improved sensitivity to family concerns), research into children's diseases, and the training of students to become the future care givers for a healthier Kentucky.

Much better than a canned institutional chronology, this is inside stuff, with earthy, sometimes humorous comments about leadership that disappointed him—and the forceful leaders he admired like pediatric heart specialist Jacqueline Noonan when she broke the glass ceiling and became department head ("don't call me "chairlady—I'm the chairman," she snapped at the dean).

Dr. Mabry was among eight young pediatricians recruited across the country in 1961, a year after the first medical students were enrolled, five years after the Legislature was persuaded by Gov. A.B. "Happy" Chandler to appropriate the initial funding of the college and medical center that would bear his name. As told by Dr. Robert Strauss in his 1997 history, "A Medical School is Born," the UK College of Medicine was one of the first of a new generation of medical schools.

Strauss, a behavioral scientist (sociology), came to the university in 1956 to help plan for the Medical Center under the leadership of the founding dean, William R. Willard. He and Mabry, among the few survivors of that era still living in Lexington, write from different viewpoints that are especially fascinating as the Medical Center undergoes an $800 million expansion and makeover a half century later—who doubts it will cost a billion dollars when finished? What these books tell us is that health care is ever changing along with new technology, the philosophy of medical education, and the increasing expectations of our society for economic and political accommodations to give everyone the best health care.

For a doctor who was also a scientist-researcher, Mabry writes with an eye for the romance and the compassion of medicine—the beginning of pediatrics in the safer milk clinics (in Lexington the Baby Milk Supply Association, founded by five prominent women in 1914 to serve babies and young children from poor families); the "signature patients," children with such distinctive problems that the young pediatricians, Mabry among them, who identified and treated them brought national attention to their new program.

Then there were administrative changes and arguments: new lab methods, conflict over outreach versus the "old school" bedside practices, the addition of formerly unwanted subspecialties, increased access which swamped the hospital and forced a new philosophy of medical education. Pediatrics, like the rest of UK, felt the strain of barriers broken over women and race, the admission of "internationals" (foreign doctors) to the faculty, dissention over physicians' pay, and finally, the impact of management change from John Oswald, a new UK president in the 1960s, and challenging visions voiced by Harry Caudill, the advocate for Appalachia.

Taking note of the controversy over universal health care legislation, which he clearly supports, Dr. Mabry offers an impassioned comment on the benefits of Medicare, Medicaid, and the investments of the Appalachian Regional Commission, all won by President Lyndon B. Johnson in his "War on Poverty." With these programs, he observes, new roads and helicopters brought in more sick folks and their kids from the mountains as UK added clinics for outreach in rural Kentucky, then more pediatric critical care, neonatal intensive care, and expanded new birth screenings, a regulation recently won by Mabry with old fashioned lobbying in Frankfort.

Although he is the senior active emeritus faculty member, Mabry welcomes the transformation away from the founders' vision of the Chandler Center as a demonstration for primary care providers to a new model—a "top 20" medical school and hospital of regional excellence in a "top 20" research university with such comprehensive services that no child will ever have to leave the Commonwealth to achieve the best care.

In a season of acrimonious politics with slandering "no nothing" rants against paying taxes or efforts to improve the nation's infrastructure and reform its education, health and energy policies, Dr. Mabry inspires us with this story. It is instructive, to reflect that the opportunity that was provided by a professional politician, Happy Chandler, who ran for governor in 1955 with a promise to build a new medical school, won the office, and kept the promise. It's also heartening to remember that Chandler's successor and political rival, Bert Combs insisted that the Center be named for Happy, lavished praise on him at the dedication, and investing millions more, declared, "I say we can afford it; actually, Kentucky cannot afford not to have it."